CALCULUS

An Introductory Approach

THE UNIVERSITY SERIES IN
UNDERGRADUATE MATHEMATICS

Editors

John L. Kelley, *University of California*
Paul R. Halmos, *University of Michigan*

A series of distinguished texts for undergraduate mathematics.
Additional titles will be listed and announced as published.

CALCULUS

An Introductory Approach

by

IVAN NIVEN

Professor of Mathematics
The University of Oregon

SECOND EDITION

D. VAN NOSTRAND COMPANY, INC.

PRINCETON, NEW JERSEY

TORONTO   LONDON

NEW YORK

D. VAN NOSTRAND COMPANY, INC.
120 Alexander St., Princeton, New Jersey (*Principal office*)
24 West 40 Street, New York 18, New York

D. VAN NOSTRAND COMPANY, LTD.
358 Kensington High Street, London, W.14, England

D. VAN NOSTRAND COMPANY (Canada), LTD.
25 Hollinger Road, Toronto 16, Canada

Published simultaneously in Canada by
D. VAN NOSTRAND COMPANY (Canada), LTD.

First Edition April 1961

Three Reprintings

Second Edition August 1966

PRINTED IN THE UNITED STATES OF AMERICA

PREFACE

The addition of new material is the primary change from the first edition of this book. Specifically, the second edition provides a fuller discussion of analytic geometry; the treatment of logarithmic functions has been expanded; formulas have been summarized at the ends of Chapters 3 to 7 for the convenience of the reader; and, most important of all, the number of problems has been increased considerably. The text has also been enhanced in many places by improved explanations.

My purpose, as in the first edition, is to present the ideas that lie at the heart of calculus, along with the necessary background material from analytic geometry. I restrict attention to a small collection of central concepts, and hence many of the topics offered in the larger books on calculus are omitted. I have aimed at a balance between theory and applications.

It is hoped that the book will be of use in situations where a brief course in calculus is wanted. For example, it should be suitable in a calculus course for liberal arts students, social science students, biological science students, or business administration students—a course designed to set forth the nature of the subject with an economy of time. Since the book grew out of lectures given at Stanford University in a special program for teachers sponsored by the General Electric Company, it should serve well courses designed for prospective and present teachers of high school mathematics. The reader should have a reasonably good knowledge of basic algebra and trigonometry, although discussions of a few topics—inequalities and radian measure, for example—have been included for convenience.

The section headings in the table of contents suffice to describe the topics considered. Special features of the book are as follows: an immediate discussion of actual problems in calculus, with a minimum of preliminaries; a simplicity of theory, relatively speaking, obtained on the one hand by restricting sharply the class of functions in the discourse and on the other hand by not attempting to state results in their most general form, or for that matter anywhere near their most general form; a development of the series expansions of the trigonometric, logarithmic, and exponential functions without the elaborate preparation that is ordinarily used; the postponing of the proof of the existence of the definite integral to an appendix, partly to break up the theory into smaller portions, and partly to keep more difficult ideas later in the presentation.

One of the most troublesome problems facing a writer of a beginning book on calculus is the matter of rigor. The difficulty is twofold: first that accuracy of statement can lead to overlengthy statements in which the reader may lose sight of the central idea in a welter of detail; second that since theorems in calculus are propositions about real numbers, ideally there should be a preamble on the logical foundations of the real number system. I have tried to avoid the first of these difficulties by a restriction, mentioned already, on the scope of the material. As to the second difficulty, I take two fundamental propositions about real numbers as axiomatic. It is assumed that a bounded sequence of increasing real numbers has a limit. The mean value theorem is also assumed without a strict proof, although a heuristic argument is given to show the plausibility of this result. These results cannot be established without a rather thorough analysis of the real number system, which is precluded by the self-imposed limitation on the length of this book.

The more difficult problems are starred. Answers to odd-numbered problems are given at the end of the book.

I was fortunate in having the manuscript read by two friendly critics of quite different backgrounds, one a university student, the other an experienced mathematician. First, I am indebted to my son Scott Niven who, in addition to making helpful suggestions about details drew my attention to certain obscure passages. Second, I am grateful to Professor Herbert S. Zuckerman for pointing out possible arrangements of the material; among other things, the final chapter was expanded considerably along lines he suggested.

IVAN NIVEN

TABLE OF CONTENTS

CHAPTER 1

WHAT IS CALCULUS ?

1.0 A short definition of calculus, in a sentence or two for example, is likely to be meaningless except to persons already familiar with the subject. The reason for this is that such a definition necessarily refers to certain mathematical operations whose nature can be known thoroughly only by prolonged examination and study. Even this book in its entirety is only a partial answer to the question "What is calculus?", because a complete answer cannot be given in a short book. A brief volume cannot encompass the elegant general results of calculus. For example, some of the topics that are treated in the later chapters of this book are approached in special ways as individual results, whereas in larger books on calculus these results are obtained as byproducts of broad sweeping theories.

In this first chapter we pose a few simple problems of calculus, with solutions given at once in some cases, but solutions postponed until later chapters in others. In diving right in, we assume that the reader has a rudimentary knowledge of inequalities and functions; these topics are elaborated in Chapter 2, but in more detail than necessary for the present chapter. Prior to the study of actual problems from calculus, there is one preliminary discussion on the concept of slope.

1.1 Slope.* The slope of a straight line is simply a measure of the steepness of rise or fall of the line, viewed from left to right. Thus the direction of a line is indicated by its slope, defined as follows. Suppose that the line makes an angle α with the x-axis, the orientation of α being from the positive end of the x-axis counterclockwise around to the line. Then the slope of the line is defined as $\tan \alpha$. If the line is

---

* Any reader with a knowledge of the concept of slope should bypass this section.

1

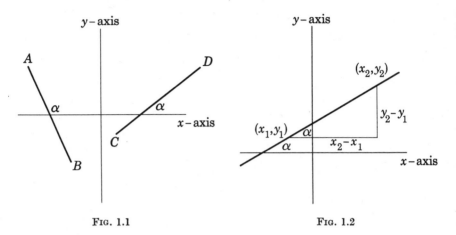

FIG. 1.1   FIG. 1.2

falling from left to right, as in the case AB in Figure 1.1, then the slope is negative, whereas if the line is rising from left to right, as in the case CD in Figure 1.1, then the slope is positive. These cases correspond to the angle α being obtuse and acute, respectively. If any two points with coordinates (x_1, y_1) and (x_2, y_2) are selected on the line, then the definition of the tangent function in trigonometry gives the well-known formula for the slope m,

$$(1) \qquad\qquad m = \tan \alpha = \frac{y_2 - y_1}{x_2 - x_1}.$$

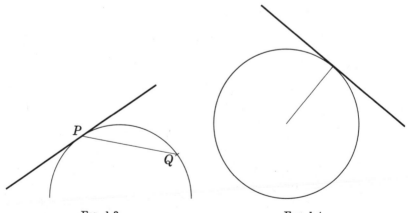

FIG. 1.3   FIG. 1.4

Any line parallel to the x-axis has $\alpha = 0°$ and $y_2 = y_1$, and the slope of such a line is zero. Any line parallel to the y-axis has $\alpha = 90°$, and so such a line has no slope because $\tan 90°$ does not exist as a real number. Another way of seeing that a vertical line has no slope is to observe that in such a case $x_2 = x_1 = 0$, and so equation (1) involves division by zero.

The slope of a curve at any point is defined as the slope of the tangent line to the curve at P. The tangent line at P, illustrated in Figure 1.3, can be described as the limiting position of the straight line PQ as the point Q is moved along the curve towards the point P. That is to say, we regard P as a fixed point and observe the nature of the straight line PQ as Q approaches P, moving along the curve. When Q coincides with P there is no line PQ, but as Q moves towards P there is a limiting position of PQ which we will be able to determine by our analysis. In the special case where the curve is a circle, a well-known theorem from elementary geometry states that the tangent line at any point is perpendicular to the radius drawn to the point of tangency, as illustrated in Figure 1.4. For curves other than the circle there is no corresponding theorem, but we shall be able with the use of calculus to determine the tangent lines of many types of curves. From these considerations we can observe that whereas a straight line has one slope, a curve has a slope at each point, and the slope is generally different from point to point.

Problems

1. Prove that the formula (1) can be written

$$m = \frac{y_1 - y_2}{x_1 - x_2}.$$

2. Find the slopes of the following lines:
   (a)   through $(0, 0)$ and $(5, 7)$;
   (b)   through $(-1, 2)$ and $(4, -6)$;
   (c)   through $(1, 2)$ and (a, b), presuming that $a \neq 1$;
   (d)   through $(2, -3)$ and $(-3, -3)$.

3. Find the numerical value of x so that the line joining $(x, -4)$ and $(6, 1)$ shall have slope 2.

4. Prove that the line joining A$(5, -7)$ and B$(6, 1)$ has the same slope as the line joining B$(6, 1)$ and C$(8, 17)$, and thus establish that the three points A, B, C are collinear.

5. Prove that the points $(4, -9)$, $(-1, -6)$, and $(-16, 3)$ are collinear.

6. Find the numerical value of y so that the point $(7, y)$ shall lie on the line joining $(1, 3)$ and $(9, 19)$.

7. Prove that the line through $(4, 2)$ and $(7, 1)$ is parallel to the line through $(5, 6)$ and $(-1, 8)$. Suggestion: two lines (not parallel to the y-axis) are parallel if and only if their slopes are equal.

8. Find the numerical value of y required so that the line through $(-2, 3)$ and $(8, 1)$ shall be parallel to the line through $(1, -4)$ and $(-4, y)$.

9. Prove that the four points $(1, -2)$, $(3, -5)$, $(8, 4)$, and $(6, 7)$ are the vertices of a parallelogram.

10. Prove that the points $(1, -2)$, $(3, -5)$, $(8, 4)$, and $(10, 1)$ are the vertices of a parallelogram.

*11. Find a point, other than $(6, 7)$ and $(10, 1)$, which forms a parallelogram along with $(1, -2)$, $(3, -5)$, and $(8, 4)$.

12. Prove that the line through $(7, 0)$ and $(10, \sqrt{3})$ is inclined to the x-axis at an angle of $30°$. (Recall that $\tan 30° = 1/\sqrt{3}$.)

13. Prove that the line through $(1, 5)$ and $(8, 12)$ is inclined to the x-axis at an angle of $45°$. (Recall that $\tan 45° = 1$.)

14. Find the slope of the line joining (a, b) and (c, d) presuming that a is not equal to c.

15. Find the slope of the line joining (a, b) and $(a+c, b+d)$, presuming that c is not equal to zero.

1.2 An Example. We now give a sample problem from differential calculus. What should be the dimensions of a cylindrical tin can of fixed volume 18π cubic inches, so that the surface area is a minimum? Since the surface area is roughly proportional to the total amount of metal in the can, the solution of the problem will give almost the dimensions for minimum cost of the metal. The figure 18π for the volume was chosen so that the arithmetic calculations would work out simply. Actually 18π cubic inches is very close to a volume of one quart.

Let r, h, S, and V denote, respectively, the radius, the height, the total surface area, and the volume of a circular cylinder. Then it will be recalled that

$$V = \pi r^2 h \quad \text{and} \quad S = 2\pi r^2 + 2\pi r h.$$

The symbol V can be replaced by the constant 18π, and so by simple algebra we can eliminate h in the formula for S,

$$18\pi = \pi r^2 h, \quad h = 18/r^2, \quad S = 2\pi r^2 + 2\pi r h,$$

$$S = 2\pi\left(r^2 + \frac{18}{r}\right).$$

Thus we have obtained S as a function of r. (It may be noted that we could have eliminated r in the algebraic process, and arrived at a formula giving S as a function of h. But square roots enter in, and so the above procedure is preferred).

---

* The more difficult problems are starred.

The graph of the function $S = 2\pi(r^2 + 18/r)$ is shown in Figure 1.5, for a reasonable set of positive values of r. To find the minimum value of S, we need some technique for locating the low point on the curve, the point labeled P in Figure 1.5. It is the point where the slope of the curve is zero. To the right of the point P the slope of the curve is positive, whereas to the left of the point P the slope of the curve is negative. The question of determining the coordinates of the point P can be settled easily by the methods of differential calculus. We are not at present in a position to finish the above problem of minimizing S, and we will return to the question later. But the example shows that some questions of maxima and minima could be handled if we knew how to calculate the slope of a curve, and so find where the slope is zero.

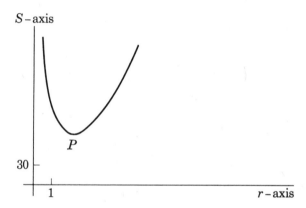

FIG. 1.5 Graph of $S = 2\pi[r^2 + 18/r]$.
(Note the different units of length on the axes.)

We have referred to the equation $S = 2\pi(r^2 + 18/r)$ as a "function" Most of the functions used in this book can be expressed as simple equations in this way, because we will work with a restricted class of functions. Furthermore in most cases our function will have a graph as in Figure 1.5, for example, or in Figure 1.6 below.

The commonly used variables in mathematics are of course y and x rather than S and r, so the functions we deal with will have equations like

$$y = x^2, \quad y = x^2 - 3x + 2, \quad y = \sqrt{x^2 - 2}.$$

When we say that y is a function of x, as in these examples, we mean simply that to each assigned numerical value of x there is a corresponding numerical value of y. In the three examples above, if we assign to x the value 3, then we get $y = 9, y = 2$, and $y = 7$, respectively. It should be noted that for many functions there are limitations on the values of x that are to be assigned. In the case of the function $y = \sqrt{x^2 - 2}$ for instance, the value $x = 0$ would not be assigned because this gives $y = \sqrt{-2}$, which is a number of a type not considered in this book. We limit our attention to real numbers, which are described briefly at the start of Chapter 2. Another example of a limitation of this sort can be seen in Figure 1.5; here we would not assign negative values to r because the radius r must be a positive number.

The graph of a function is a pictorial representation of the function by use of a coordinate system. It is easier to conceive a function in its graphical form than in a more abstract way as a correspondence between sets of numbers. For this reason we will approach functions through their graphs wherever possible.

It will also be necessary to think of functions in a general sense. Just as the symbol x is used to denote an arbitrary number, so the notation $f(x)$ is used to denote an arbitrary function. Thus $f(x)$, read "f of x", is a general notation for a function of x. The corresponding equation is $y = f(x)$. For a specific function like $y = x^2 - 3x + 2$, we can also write $f(x) = x^2 - 3x + 2$. Then in turn x can be specified, for example

$$f(5) = 5^2 - 3 \cdot 5 + 2 = 12, \quad f(9) = 9^2 - 3 \cdot 9 + 2 = 56.$$

These sketchy remarks on the idea of a function will suffice for this chapter. A fuller discussion is given in § 2.5.

Problems

1. In the analysis of the cylindrical tin can a formula was derived for S as a function of r. Derive a formula for S as a function of h.

2. Draw the graph of $y = 4x - 3$ on a coordinate axis system.

3. Sketch the graph of $y = x^2 - 1$, using a succession of integer values of x from $x = -5$ to $x = 5$. (The integers are the numbers $0, 1, -1, 2, -2, 3, -3, 4, -4, \ldots$.)

4. Sketch the graph of $y = 7 - x^2$.

5. Given $f(x) = x^2 - 3x + 2$, compute $f(7), f(-7), f(0)$ and $f(-3)$.

6. In the case $f(x) = 12 + x - x^2$, find the values of $f(0), f(1), f(-4), f(5/2)$, and $f(-8)$.

7. For the function $f(x) = x^3 - 3$, evaluate $f(2), f(-2), f(0), f(-3)$, and $f(1/2)$.

1.3 The Slope of a Special Curve. We turn to a much simpler equation than $S = 2\pi(r^2 + 18/r)$ to begin our treatment of the slope of a curve. The problem now is to find the slope of the curve $y = x^2$

at the point (3, 9). The parabolic equation $y = x^2$ is about the simplest among non-linear equations, and so provides a good starting point. As in Figure 1.6, let us denote the point (3, 9) by A, and let P be any nearby point on the curve. Since the point P, unlike A, is not a fixed point, we give it coordinates (x, x^2). This is nothing but the general coordinates (x, y) with y replaced by x^2 in accordance with the presumption that P is a point on the curve $y = x^2$. The slope of the chord AP, by formula (1) of § 1.1, is $(x^2 - 9)/(x - 3)$. The tangent line to the curve $y = x^2$ at A is the limiting position of the chord AP as the point P approaches the point A. Thus the slope of the tangent line at A, which by definition is the same as the slope of the curve at A, is the limiting value of $(x^2 - 9)/(x - 3)$ as x approaches 3. We cannot simply substitute $x = 3$, because (i) geometrically the points P and A coincide and there is no chord AP, and (ii) algebraically the expression $(x^2 - 9)/(x - 3)$ becomes $0/0$, which has no meaning.

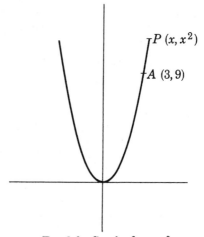

Now by elementary algebra we have

$$\frac{x^2 - 9}{x - 3} = \frac{(x+3)(x-3)}{x-3} = x+3,$$

FIG. 1.6 Graph of $y = x^2$.

and $(x^2 - 9)/(x - 3)$ is indeed equal to $x + 3$ for all values of x except one, namely $x = 3$. The function $f(x) = x + 3$ has a straight line graph as shown in Figure 1.7 when plotted in the usual fashion with a horizontal x-axis and a vertical y-axis. The function $F(x) = (x^2 - 9)/(x - 3)$

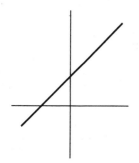

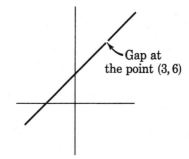

Gap at the point (3, 6)

FIG. 1.7 Graph of $f(x) = x+3$.   FIG. 1.8 Graph of $f(x) = (x^2-9)/(x-3)$.

has virtually the same graph but with a point missing, a gap at (3, 6). It is clear intuitively that the limit of $(x^2 - 9)/(x - 3)$ as x approaches 3 is the same as the limit of $x + 3$ as x approaches 3. We shall spell out a precise definition of limit later. In the meantime we write the standard notation for limits

$$\lim_{x \to 3} \frac{x^2 - 9}{x - 3} = \lim_{x \to 3} (x + 3) = 6,$$

where "lim" stands for "limit", and "$x \to 3$" is short for "as x approaches 3". We notice that while $(x^2 - 9)/(x - 3)$ has no value at $x = 3$, nevertheless it has a limit as x approaches 3. This limiting value 6 is thus the slope of the curve $y = x^2$ at the point (3, 9).

It is instructive also to consider a set of values of $(x^2 - 9)/(x - 3)$ as $x \to 3$:

x	$(x^2 - 9)/(x - 3)$
3.1	6.1
3.01	6.01
3.001	6.001
3.0001	6.0001
$3 + 10^{-10}$	$6 + 10^{-10}$

This table of values suggests the germ of the idea of limit, namely that

$$\lim_{x \to 3} \frac{x^2 - 9}{x - 3} = 6$$

means that $(x^2 - 9)/(x - 3)$ gets closer and closer to 6 as x approaches 3. We shall formulate this technically in the next chapter.

Problems

1. Find the slope of the curve $y = 2x^2$ at the point (3, 18).
2. Find the slope of the curve $y = x^2$ at the point (2, 4).
3. Find the slope of the curve $y = x^2$ at the point (1, 1).
4. Find the slope of the curve $y = x^2$ at the point $(-3, 9)$.
5. Solve the preceding problem by using the information that the slope of the curve $y = x^2$ is 6 at the point (3, 9), and the fact that the graph of the curve is symmetric about the y-axis.
6. Find the slope of the curve $y = -x^2$ at the point $(5, -25)$.
7. What is the slope of the curve $y = x^2 + 6$ at the point where $x = 6$?
8. What would be the expected value of the slope of $y = x^2$ at $(0, 0)$? Check this value by the limit procedure.
9. Find the slope of $y = x^2 + x$ at (1, 2).
*10. What is the slope of the curve $y = x^3$ at the point (3, 27)?

1.4 The Notation for a Sum. Before giving an example in integral calculus, we introduce the mathematical notation for a sum. Consider the sum of the integers from 1 to 100,

$$1+2+3+4+\ldots+98+99+100.$$

This is written

$$\sum_{j=1}^{100} j,$$

meaning the sum of integers j ranging from $j = 1$ to $j = 100$. Notice that j plays a dummy role here, and we could just as well write

$$\sum_{k=1}^{100} k \quad \text{or} \quad \sum_{i=1}^{100} i \quad \text{or} \quad \sum_{h=1}^{100} h.$$

If we wanted to indicate the sum of the integers from 7 to 100, we would write

$$7+8+9+\ldots+98+99+100 = \sum_{j=7}^{100} j \quad \text{or} \quad \sum_{k=7}^{100} k \quad \text{or} \quad \sum_{i=7}^{100} i.$$

If the sum of the square of the integers from 7 to 100 were desired, then we would write

$$7^2+8^2+9^2+\ldots+98^2+99^2+100^2 = \sum_{j=7}^{100} j^2.$$

In general, if m and n are any two integers with $m < n$ and if $f(x)$ is a function which is defined (i.e., has meaning) for all the integers from m to n, then

$$\sum_{j=m}^{n} f(j)$$

is an abbreviated way of writing the sum

$$f(m)+f(m+1)+f(m+2)+\ldots+f(n-1)+f(n).$$

Here are some more examples:

$$\sum_{j=10}^{15} j^3 = 10^3+11^3+12^3+13^3+14^3+15^3;$$

$$\sum_{j=3}^{80} j(j+1) = 3\cdot4+4\cdot5+5\cdot6+\ldots+89\cdot90+90\cdot91;$$

$$\sum_{k=20}^{70} k^2 = 20^2 + 21^2 + 22^2 + \ldots + 69^2 + 70^2;$$

$$\sum_{k=20}^{70} (k^2 + 1) = 20^2 + 1 + 21^2 + 1 + 22^2 + 1 + \ldots + 69^2 + 1 + 70^2 + 1;$$

$$\sum_{j=1}^{n} j^2 = 1^2 + 2^2 + 3^2 + \ldots + (n-1)^2 + n^2.$$

Problems

Which of the following are correct, and which incorrect? Give reasons for each conclusion.

1. $\displaystyle\sum_{k=20}^{70} (k^2 + 1) = 51 + \sum_{k=20}^{70} k^2.$

2. $\displaystyle\sum_{j=1}^{100} j^2 = 100 + \sum_{j=1}^{99} j^2.$

3. $\displaystyle\sum_{j=1}^{100} j^2 = 1 + \sum_{j=2}^{100} j^2.$

4. $\displaystyle\sum_{j=1}^{100} j^2 = 10001 + \sum_{j=2}^{99} j^2.$

5. $\displaystyle\sum_{j=1}^{n} j^2 = n^2 + \sum_{j=1}^{n-1} j^2.$

6. $\displaystyle\sum_{j=1}^{100} (2 + j) = 2 + \sum_{j=1}^{100} j.$

7. $\displaystyle\sum_{j=1}^{100} 2 = 200.$

8. $\displaystyle\sum_{j=1}^{n} 1 = n.$

9. $\displaystyle\sum_{j=1}^{n} 3j^2 = 3 \sum_{j=1}^{n} j^2.$

10. $\displaystyle\sum_{j=0}^{n} j = \sum_{j=1}^{n} j.$

11. $\displaystyle\sum_{j=0}^{n} (j + 1) = \sum_{j=1}^{n} (j + 1).$

12. $\displaystyle\sum_{j=1}^{n} \frac{j}{c} = \frac{1}{c} \sum_{j=1}^{n} j,$

where c is a constant, not zero.

13. $\displaystyle\sum_{j=1}^{10} j^3 = \sum_{j=1}^{10} j \cdot \sum_{j=1}^{10} j^2.$

14. $\displaystyle\sum_{j=1}^{99} (50-j) = \sum_{j=1}^{99} (j-50).$

15. $\displaystyle\sum_{j=1}^{n} n^2 j^2 = n^2 \sum_{j=1}^{n} j^2.$

1.5 Some Special Sums. It is well known that the sum of the positive integers from 1 to n is equal to $n(n+1)/2$, thus

(2) $$\sum_{j=1}^{n} j = \frac{n(n+1)}{2}.$$

Although this is commonly proved in elementary mathematics by the use of arithmetic progressions, we give here a proof by a method of differences, sometimes called the method of telescoping sums. The equation

$$(x+1)^2 - x^2 = 2x+1$$

is an identity in x, that is, it is true for every value of x. Replace x successively by $x = 1, 2, 3, \ldots, n$ to get the n equations

$$2^2 - 1^2 = 2 \cdot 1 + 1$$
$$3^2 - 2^2 = 2 \cdot 2 + 1$$
$$4^2 - 3^2 = 2 \cdot 3 + 1$$
$$\cdots$$
$$n^2 - (n-1)^2 = 2(n-1) + 1$$
$$(n+1)^2 - n^2 = 2n + 1.$$

We add these equations, noting the extensive cancellation on the left, to get

$$(n+1)^2 - 1^2 = \sum_{j=1}^{n} 2j + \sum_{j=1}^{n} 1 = \sum_{j=1}^{n} 2j + n.$$

We note that

$$(n+1)^2 - 1^2 = n^2 + 2n, \quad \text{and} \quad \sum_{j=1}^{n} 2j = 2 \sum_{j=1}^{n} j,$$

and substituting these we get

$$n^2 + 2n = 2 \sum_{j=1}^{n} j + n, \quad 2 \sum_{j=1}^{n} j = n^2 + n = n(n+1).$$

Dividing by 2, we obtain formula (2).

Next we prove by a similar method that

(3)
$$\sum_{j=1}^{n} j^2 = \frac{1}{3}n^3 + \frac{1}{2}n^2 + \frac{1}{6}n.$$

To establish this, we begin by noting that a simple expansion of $(x+1)^3$ leads to the identity

$$(x+1)^3 - x^3 = 3x^2 + 3x + 1.$$

Substituting $x = 1, 2, 3, 4, \ldots, n$ we get n equations

$$2^3 - 1^3 = 3 \cdot 1^2 + 3 \cdot 1 + 1$$
$$3^3 - 2^3 = 3 \cdot 2^2 + 3 \cdot 2 + 1$$
$$\cdots$$
$$n^3 - (n-1)^3 = 3(n-1)^2 + 3(n-1) + 1$$
$$(n+1)^3 - n^3 = 3n^2 + 3n + 1.$$

Adding, and noting the cancellation of terms on the left, we get

$$(n+1)^3 - 1^3 = 3 \sum_{j=1}^{n} j^2 + 3 \sum_{j=1}^{n} j + \sum_{j=1}^{n} 1.$$

From elementary algebra, and from formula (2), we get

$$(n+1)^3 = n^3 + 3n^2 + 3n + 1, \quad 3 \sum_{j=1}^{n} j = \frac{3n(n+1)}{2}, \quad \sum_{j=1}^{n} 1 = n,$$

and hence

$$n^3 + 3n^2 + 3n = \frac{3n(n+1)}{2} + n + 3 \sum_{j=1}^{n} j^2.$$

This reduces to formula (3), by some such steps as

$$3 \sum j^2 = n^3 + 3n^2 + 3n - \frac{3n(n+1)}{2} - n = n^3 + \frac{3n^2}{2} + \frac{n}{2},$$

$$\sum j^2 = \frac{1}{3}n^3 + \frac{1}{2}n^2 + \frac{1}{6}n.$$

Problems

1. Find the value of $1+2+3+4+\ldots+1000$.
2. Find the value of $1^2+2^2+3^2+4^2+\ldots+100^2$.
3. Find the value of $50^2+51^2+52^2+\ldots+100^2$.
4. Evaluate the sum

$$\sum_{k=1}^{n} k^2.$$

5. Prove that

$$\sum_{j=1}^{n-1} j = \frac{n(n-1)}{2}.$$

6. Prove that

$$\sum_{j=1}^{n} j^2 = \frac{n}{6}(n+1)(2n+1).$$

7. Evaluate the sums

(a) $\displaystyle\sum_{j=1}^{n-1} j^2$;   (b) $\displaystyle\sum_{j=0}^{n-2} j^2$.

8. Evaluate the sums

(a) $\displaystyle\sum_{j=1}^{n} 12j^2$;   (b) $\displaystyle\sum_{j=1}^{n} nj^2$;   (c) $\displaystyle\sum_{j=1}^{n} n^2j^2$.

9. Prove that

$$\sum_{j=1}^{n} (j-1)^2 = \sum_{j=1}^{n-1} j^2.$$

10. Evaluate the sums

(a) $\displaystyle\sum_{j=1}^{n} (3j+3j^2)$;   (b) $\displaystyle\sum_{j=1}^{n} (nj+n^2j^2)$.

11. Verify the identity $(x+1)^4-x^4 = 4x^3+6x^2+4x+1$.
*12. Use the identity of the preceding question to find a formula for

$$\sum_{j=1}^{n} j^3.$$

1.6 An Example from Integral Calculus. We shall now use the algebraic preamble above to calculate the area bounded by a parabolic arc and straight lines. The problem we solve was settled by the Greeks in ancient times, but their methods were by comparison more difficult and less suited to generalization to other problems.

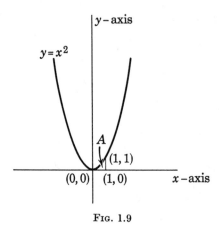

FIG. 1.9

Consider the parabola $y = x^2$, that is, the collection of points whose coordinates satisfy this equation. In particular, we are interested in the portion of the curve between $(0, 0)$ and $(1, 1)$. The problem is to find the area A of the configuration bounded above by the curve, below by the x-axis from $(0, 0)$ to $(1, 0)$, and on the right by the line joining $(1, 0)$ and $(1, 1)$. Calling the line segment from $(0, 0)$ to $(1, 0)$ the baseline, we divide it into a whole number n of equal parts, each of length $1/n$. The division points are

$$(0, 0), \left(\frac{1}{n}, 0\right), \left(\frac{2}{n}, 0\right), \dots, \left(\frac{n-1}{n}, 0\right) \left(\frac{n}{n}, 0.\right)$$

Drawing vertical lines from these points on the baseline, we construct a pattern of rectangles as in Figure 1.10. On each segment of the baseline there stand two rectangles. For example, on B_1B_2 there stand the lower rectangle $B_1B_2C_2C_1$, and the upper rectangle $B_1B_2D_2D_1$. Since

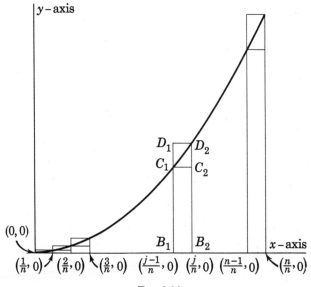

FIG. 1.10

the points C_1 and D_2 are on the curve $y = x^2$, their coordinates are

$$C_1 : \left(\frac{j-1}{n}, \frac{(j-1)^2}{n^2}\right); \quad D_2 : \left(\frac{j}{n}, \frac{j^2}{n^2}\right).$$

Because the base segment B_1B_2 has length $1/n$, we have the area formulas

$$\text{area } B_1B_2C_2C_1 = \frac{1}{n} \cdot \frac{(j-1)^2}{n^2} = \frac{(j-1)^2}{n^3},$$

and

$$\text{area } B_1B_2D_2D_1 = \frac{1}{n} \cdot \frac{j^2}{n^2} = \frac{j^2}{n^3}.$$

The sum of the areas of the lower rectangles is less than the area A under the parabola, whereas the sum of the upper rectangles is greater than A. In symbols, we have*

(4)
$$\sum_{j=1}^{n} \frac{(j-1)^2}{n^3} < A < \sum_{j=1}^{n} \frac{j^2}{n^3}.$$

The n^3 can be factored out of each sum, and applying formula (3) of § 1.5 we get

$$\sum_{j=1}^{n} \frac{j^2}{n^3} = \frac{1}{n^3} \sum_{j=1}^{n} j^2 = \frac{1}{n^3}\left(\frac{1}{3}n^3 + \frac{1}{2}n^2 + \frac{1}{6}n\right)$$

$$= \frac{1}{3} + \frac{1}{2n} + \frac{1}{6n^2},$$

$$\sum_{j=1}^{n} \frac{(j-1)^2}{n^3} = \frac{1}{n^3} \sum_{j=1}^{n} (j-1)^2 = \frac{1}{n^3} \sum_{k-1}^{n-1} k^2 = \frac{1}{n^3}\left(\sum_{k=1}^{n} k^2 - n^2\right)$$

$$= \frac{1}{n^3}\left(\frac{1}{3}n^3 + \frac{1}{2}n^2 + \frac{1}{6}n - n^2\right) = \frac{1}{3} - \frac{1}{2n} + \frac{1}{6n^2}.$$

Thus the above inequalities can be written

(5)
$$\frac{1}{3} - \frac{1}{2n} + \frac{1}{6n^2} < A < \frac{1}{3} + \frac{1}{2n} + \frac{1}{6n^2},$$

---

* It is presumed that the reader is familiar with the symbol $<$, which is used in this chapter in its simplest aspect. In later chapters more elaborate use is made of inequalities, and so a treatment of this topic is given in § 2.1.

and we shall see that A is thus trapped between values which get arbitrarily close to 1/3 as n increases indefinitely.

The expression on the left of (5) can be written in the form

$$\frac{1}{3} - \frac{1}{2n} + \frac{1}{6n^2} = \frac{1}{3} - \frac{1}{2n}\left(\frac{3n-1}{3n}\right)$$

and since $1/2n$ and $(3n-1)/3n$ are positive, this shows that

$$\frac{1}{3} - \frac{1}{2n} + \frac{1}{6n^2} < \frac{1}{3}.$$

But though the expression on the left of (5) is less than 1/3, we see that we can make it as close to 1/3 as we please, because as n gets very large, $1/2n$ and $1/6n^2$ get very small. We can state this in another way by saying that as n tends to infinity, $1/2n$ and $1/6n^2$ tend to zero, in symbols thus

$$\lim_{n\to\infty} \frac{1}{2n} = 0, \quad \lim_{n\to\infty} \frac{1}{6n^2} = 0, \quad \lim_{n\to\infty}\left(\frac{1}{3} - \frac{1}{2n} + \frac{1}{6n^2}\right) = \frac{1}{3}.$$

The meaning of these statements will be made more precise in the next chapter. For the present, we see that also

$$\lim_{n\to\infty}\left(\frac{1}{3} + \frac{1}{2n} + \frac{1}{6n^2}\right) = \frac{1}{3},$$

and so from (5) we can conclude that $A = 1/3$.

We have used limiting processes to compute the area A. It should not be concluded that the only application of integral calculus is to the calculation of areas. The principal concept is not the area, but the limit of a sum—in our example the limit of a sum of areas of lower rectangles and the limit of a sum of areas of upper rectangles. The idea of a limit of a sum occurs in many forms throughout advanced mathematics.

Problems

1. Find the area bounded by the parabola $y = x^2$ from $(0,0)$ to $(1,1)$, the y-axis from $(0,0)$ to $(0,1)$, and the straight line from $(0,1)$ to $(1,1)$. Suggestion: use the answer $A = 1/3$ from § 1.6.

2. Find the area bounded by the parabola $y = x^2$ and the straight line joining the points $(1,1)$ and $(-1,1)$.

3. Find the area enclosed between the parabola $y = x^2$ and the straight line $y = x$.

4. Find the area bounded by the parabola $y = 1+x^2$ from $(0,1)$ to $(1,2)$, and by the three straight-line segments from $(1,2)$ to $(1,0)$, from $(1,0)$ to $(0,0)$, and from $(0,0)$ to $(0,1)$.

*5. Find the area bounded by the parabola $y = x^2$ from $(0, 0)$ to $(2, 4)$, the straight line from $(0, 0)$ to $(2, 0)$, and the straight line from $(2, 0)$ to $(2, 4)$.

*6. Find the area bounded by the parabola $y = 3x^2$ from $(0, 0)$ to $(1, 3)$, the straight line from $(0, 0)$ to $(1, 0)$, and the straight line from $(1, 0)$ to $(1, 3)$.

*7. Find the area bounded by the parabola $y = 3x^2$ from $(0, 0)$ to $(2, 12)$, the straight line from $(0, 0)$ to $(2, 0)$, and the straight line from $(2, 0)$ to $(2, 12)$.

1.7 A Refinement. We took the position in the preceding section that we knew in some sense what is meant by the "area" of a configuration bounded partly by a curve. However, that was a little naive, as the following argument demonstrates. The idea of area is first introduced in terms of a square unit, that is, the area of a square each of whose sides is of unit length. For example, if the unit of length is an

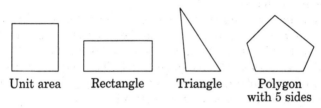

Unit area   Rectangle   Triangle   Polygon
                                       with 5 sides

FIG. 1.11

inch, we are talking about one square inch. From this unit of area we extend the concept to the area of any rectangle, and thence to any triangle, and from there to any figure that can be triangulated, namely any polygon. We do not propose to go through the steps of this development, but we draw attention to the essential difficulty that arises at the next step, when we introduce figures bounded, at least in part, by curved lines. What is meant by the area of such a figure? This question is not answered in this book, but we do point out the direction the answer takes. The point is this: whereas in § 1.6 we talked simply as though we had a computation to perform, the whole process should have been separated into (i) a discussion of the *definition* of area in terms of the limit of a sum of rectangles, as in Figure 1.10, and (ii) the subsequent computation based on such a definition. This separation of the problem of area into two parts is a relatively modern development in mathematics.

1.8 Other Results from Analytic Geometry. The concept of slope from analytic geometry, discussed in § 1.1, is a central idea in the study of calculus. A few other basic ideas from geometry will be helpful, partly for use in developing the theory, but more in the solving of problems. These results, perhaps quite familiar to the reader, are given without proof.

A linear equation in x and y, like $4x - 7y = 35$, represents a straight line when graphed or plotted on a plane with a pair of perpendicular coordinate axes. The general linear equation in x and y can be denoted by $ax + by = c$, where a and b are not both zero. If $a = 0$ the equation has the form $by = c$ or $y = c/b$, and in this case the straight line is parallel to the x-axis. If $b = 0$ the equation has the form $ax = c$ or $x = c/a$, and the straight line is parallel to the y-axis. For example, the straight line passing through $(3, 5)$ parallel to the x-axis has equation $y = 5$. Similarly, the straight line through $(3, 5)$ parallel to the y-axis has equation $x = 3$. The x-axis itself has equation $y = 0$, and the y-axis has equation $x = 0$.

A straight line with equation $ax + by = c$ has slope $-a/b$, but this is valid only if $b \neq 0$. Thus a line parallel to the y-axis has no slope assigned to it. The straight line $4x - 7y = 35$ has slope $4/7$ and the straight line $4x + 7y = 35$ has slope $-4/7$. The slope turns up as the coefficient of x when the equation is solved for y, as for example when $4x - 7y = 35$ and $4x + 7y = 35$ are reformulated as

$$y = \frac{4}{7}x - 5 \quad \text{and} \quad y = -\frac{4}{7}x + 5.$$

Two lines with slopes m_1 and m_2 are perpendicular if $m_1 m_2 = -1$, or what is the same thing $m_1 = -1/m_2$. Two lines with slopes m_1 and m_2 are parallel if $m_1 = m_2$.

An equation of a line can be determined if enough information is available, for example the coordinates of two points on the line, or the slope of the line and the coordinates of one point. If the line has slope m and passes through the point (x_1, y_1), an equation is

$$y - y_1 = m(x - x_1).$$

For example an equation of the line with slope 3 passing through the point $(4, 7)$ is $y - 7 = 3(x - 4)$ or $y = 3x - 5$. In the other case mentioned, if the line passes through the two points (x_1, y_1) and (x_2, y_2) an equation is

$$\frac{y - y_1}{y_1 - y_2} = \frac{x - x_1}{x_1 - x_2}.$$

This formulation is not valid if $x_1 = x_2$ or $y_1 = y_2$ because division by zero occurs. However, if the equation is written in the form

$$(x_1 - x_2)(y - y_1) = (y_1 - y_2)(x - x_1),$$

it is valid in all cases of two given points.

The coordinate axes separate the plane into four *quadrants*: the *first* quadrant where points have positive coordinates; the *second* quadrant where coordinates of points are of opposite sign, with x negative and y positive; the *third* quadrant where points have negative coordinates; and the *fourth* quadrant where coordinates of points are of opposite sign, with x positive and y negative.

The distance between the points (x_1, y_1) and (x_2, y_2) is

$$\sqrt{(x_2 - x_1)^2 + (y_2 - y_1)^2}.$$

This result is in effect the theorem of Pythagoras formulated in the language of analytic geometry. A circle with center at the origin $(0, 0)$ and radius r has equation $x^2 + y^2 = r^2$, and a circle of the same radius with center at (h, k) has equation

$$(x - h)^2 + (y - k)^2 = r^2.$$

For example an equation of the circle with center at $(0, 0)$ and radius 3 is $x^2 + y^2 = 9$. If we solve this equation for y in terms of x we can separate it into the two equations

$$y = \sqrt{9 - x^2} \quad \text{and} \quad y = -\sqrt{9 - x^2}.$$

The first of these represents the upper half of the circle with positive and zero values for y, and the second represents the lower half with negative and zero values for y.

The intersection points of lines and curves can be determined by solving their equations. For example the fact that the lines $2x - 3y = 9$ and $x + 5y = -2$ intersect at the point $(3, -1)$ can be obtained by solving the equations simultaneously to get $x = 3$, $y = -1$. Similarly by solving the equations $y = x^2$ and $y = x + 2$ we get the intersection points $(2, 4)$ and $(-1, 1)$.

Problems

1. Find the slopes of the lines (a) $x - y = 5$; (b) $2x + 3y = 0$; (c) $y = 8$.

2. Draw sketches of the lines in the preceding question on the same set of coordinate axes.

3. Consider the line $4x - 7y = 35$. By setting $x = 0$ and $y = 0$, one at a time, and solving first for y and then for x, show that $(0, 5)$ and $(35/4, 0)$ are points on the line. Then use formula (1) of § 1.1 to verify that the slope of the line is $4/7$.

4. Generalize the procedure in the preceding problem to prove by use of formula (1) of § 1.1 that the slope of the line $ax + by = c$ is $-a/b$. Assume that $a \neq 0$ and $b \neq 0$.

5. Check the details on the solution of the equations $2x-3y = 9$ and $x+5y = -2$ as given in the text above. Do the same for the equations $y = x^2$ and $y = x+2$.

6. Two of the following lines are parallel and two are perpendicular. Identify the pairs: (a) $6x-3y = 5$; (b) $3x-5y = 6$; (c) $10y = 6x+11$; (d) $x+2y+7 = 0$.

7. By solving $x-y+3 = 0$ and $y = 4x^2$ simultaneously, find the points of intersection of the graphs of the equations. Sketch the graphs on the same set of coordinate axes.

8. Find the coordinates of the point of intersection of the lines $x+3y = 7$ and $3x+y = 5$.

9. Which of the points $(4, -3)$, $(6, 2)$, $(1, 7)$, $(-2, 17)$, $(-1, 13)$ lie on the line $10x+3y = 31$?

10. Find an equation of the line with slope $1/2$ passing through the point $(2, 1)$.

11. Find an equation of the line through the two points $(7, 4)$ and $(2, -1)$.

12. Find an equation of the line through the two points $(-2, 4)$ and $(-2, 7)$.

13. Find an equation of the circle of diameter 10 with center at the origin $(0, 0)$. Does the point $(-3, 4)$ lie on this circle?

14. Find the slope of the tangent line to the circle $x^2+y^2 = 25$ at the point $(3, 4)$. Also find an equation of the tangent line. Suggestion: Use the fact from elementary geometry that the tangent line is perpendicular to the radius drawn from the center to the point of tangency $(3, 4)$.

15. Find an equation of the tangent line to the parabola $y = x^2$ at the point $(3, 9)$. Suggestion: The slope of this tangent line was determined in § 1.3.

CHAPTER 2

LIMITS

2.0. From the sample problems of the preceding chapter, it is clear that calculus is based on limiting processes, and so we now discuss the question of limits at some length. The theory of limits, in turn, is based on inequalities between real numbers. Whereas a lengthy treatise on calculus will ordinarily begin with an analysis of the real number system, the following observations must suffice for us.

Let a straight line be marked off with coordinates, after the fashion of the x-axis in coordinate geometry. That is, a zero point and a unit length are chosen, and this unit length is used to determine the location of the points marked 1, 2, 3, 4, ... on one side of the zero point, and the points marked -1, -2, -3, -4, ... on the other side.

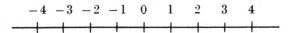

Then to each point on the line there belongs a number which apart from sign denotes the distance of that point from the origin. The collection of all such numbers constitutes the system of real numbers, and when we refer to a "number" in this book, the referent is one of these real numbers.

Continuing our intuitive description of real numbers, we observe that all numbers belonging to points on the right side (the same side as the point 1) are positive, and all on the left side are negative. By a non-negative number is meant one which is positive or zero. We shall take as axiomatic—without proof, that is—the following properties of real numbers:

    (a) both the sum and the product of two positive numbers are positive numbers;

    (b) the sum of two negative numbers is negative, but their product is positive;

(c) the product of a positive number and a negative number is negative;

(d) for any real number a, $a+0 = a$, $a \cdot 0 = 0$, and $a \cdot 1 = a$;

(e) the sum and product of two non-negative numbers are non-negative;

(f) the sum of a positive number and a non-negative number is positive.

If two numbers a and b are equal we write $a = b$, and if they are not equal we write $a \neq b$. If two or more mathematical statements imply one another, we say that they are equivalent. For example, the four equations $x = y$, $y = x$, $x-y = 0$ and $y-x = 0$ are equivalent. If $a \neq 0$ then a^{-1} or $1/a$ is called the inverse or the reciprocal of a.

2.1. Inequalities. The verbal statement that 2 is less than 4 is written mathematically in the form $2 < 4$. This can also be written $4 > 2$, i.e., 4 is greater than 2. These inequality signs are also used with variables; for example $x > 2$ states that x is greater than 2. The notation $x \geq 2$ states that x is greater than or equal to 2.

DEFINITION. *The inequalities $x > y$ and $y < x$ are equivalent, and they mean $x-y$ is positive, or, what is the same thing, $y-x$ is negative. Thus the following four inequalities are equivalent:*

$$x > y, \quad y < x, \quad x-y > 0, \quad y-x < 0.$$

Similarly $x \geq y$ means that $x-y$ is positive or zero, and the following four inequalities are equivalent:

$$x \geq y, \quad y \leq x, \quad x-y \geq 0, \quad y-x \leq 0.$$

That the sum and product of two positive numbers are positive can be written mathematically as follows:

If $a > 0$ and $b > 0$, then $a+b > 0$ and $ab > 0$.

Other statements in the preamble preceding this section can be written as inequalities, notably these:

If $a \geq 0$ and $b \geq 0$, then $a+b \geq 0$ and $ab \geq 0$;

if $a \geq 0$ and $b > 0$, then $a+b > 0$.

THEOREM 1. *If $a > b$ and $b > c$, then $a > c$.*

PROOF. From the definition we see that $a-b$ and $b-c$ are positive, so their sum $(a-b)+(b-c)$ is also positive. Thus $a-c$ is positive, and hence $a > c$.

THEOREM 2. *If $a > b$ then $a+c > b+c$ and $a-c > b-c$ for any number c. If $a > b$, and c is positive, then $ac > bc$.*

PROOF. Since $a+c > b+c$ amounts to $(a+c)-(b+c) > 0$, and so to $a-b > 0$, we see that it follows from $a > b$. A similar argument applies to the second conclusion. To see that $ac > bc$, we note that $a-b$ and c are both positive, and so is their product $ac-bc$. Thus all parts of the theorem are established.

THEOREM 3. *Inequalities can be added. If $a > b$ and $c > d$, then $a+c > b+d$.*

PROOF. Since $a-b$ and $c-d$ are positive, so is their sum $(a-b) +(c-d)$. Hence we have

$$(a+c)-(b+d) > 0, \quad a+c > b+d.$$

THEOREM 4. *Inequalities can be multiplied sometimes. If $a > b$ and $c > d$, and if b and d are non-negative, then $ac > bd$.*

PROOF. Since $a > b$ and b is non-negative, it follows that a is positive. Similarly c is positive. We separate the proof into two cases, $b = 0$ and $b > 0$. In case $b = 0$ then $bd = 0$, but ac is positive, so $ac > bd$.

In case $b > 0$, we apply Theorem 2 to $c > d$ and b to get $bc > bd$. We also apply Theorem 2 to $a > b$ and c, to get $ac > bc$. Hence by Theorem 1, $ac > bd$.

THEOREM 5. *The inequalities $a > b$ and $-a < -b$ are equivalent.*

PROOF. Each inequality means that $a-b$ is positive.

Note that this theorem says in effect that an inequality is reversed if both sides are multiplied by -1. A similar effect is produced (sometimes) by taking reciprocals:

THEOREM 6. *If a and b are positive, then the inequalities*

$$a > b \quad and \quad \frac{1}{a} < \frac{1}{b}$$

are equivalent.

PROOF. Applying the last part of Theorem 2 with $(ab)^{-1}$ playing the role of c, we get

$$a(ab)^{-1} > b(ab)^{-1}, \quad \frac{1}{b} > \frac{1}{a}.$$

Conversely, if we assume that $(1/b) > (1/a)$, we can multiply both sides of this inequality by ab to get $a > b$.

It may be noted that Theorems 1 to 6 remain valid if each inequality sign $>$ or $<$ is replaced by $\geqq$ or $\leqq$ respectively. The reason for this is that the only principles used in the proofs of these theorems are that the sum and the product of two positive numbers are positive. But we can replace these by the principles that the sum and the product of two non-negative numbers are non-negative. This is all that we need to observe, because $a \geqq b$ is equivalent to $a - b \geqq 0$, and it means that $a - b$ is non-negative.

One of the principal uses that we will have for inequalities is to designate sets of values. If we want to indicate that x is positive we can write $x > 0$. If we want to say that y is non-negative, we can write $y \geqq 0$, or what is the same thing, $0 \leqq y$. Again, if we want to say that x lies strictly between 3 and 7, we can write $3 < x < 7$. If x lies between 3 and 7 with the end values included, we write $3 \leqq x \leqq 7$. Another useful device for indicating sets of numbers is the notion of absolute value, which we discuss in the next section.

Problems

1. Give a numerical example to show that the second sentence of Theorem 2 does not hold if the restriction "c is positive" is removed.

2. Give an example to show that "if $a > b$ and $c > d$ then $ac > bd$" does not hold under all circumstances. (Compare this with Theorem 4).

3. Give an example to show that Theorem 6 does not hold if the restriction "a and b are positive" is removed.

4. Prove that if $a \geqq b$ and $b > c$ then $a > c$.

5. Prove that if $a \geqq b$ and $c > d$ then $a + c > b + d$. If furthermore b and d are positive, prove that $ac > bd$.

6. Prove that $1/n^2 < 1/n$ holds for every positive integer n, with one exception.

7. If the temperature T in the last 24 hours ranged from 50 to 80 degrees, show that this can be written mathematically in the form $50 \leqq T \leqq 80$. Show that an alternative way of writing this is $-15 \leqq T - 65 \leqq 15$.

8. Given that T satisfies the inequalities $-20 \leqq T - 62 \leqq 20$, what are the smallest and largest possible values of T?

*9. Let a and b be two different numbers. (This is written mathematically $a \neq b$.) Prove that $a^2 + b^2 > 2ab$. Suggestion: $a - b$ is not zero, so $(a - b)^2$ is positive.

*10. Let c and d be positive numbers. Their arithmetic mean is $(c + d)/2$, and their geometric mean is $\sqrt{cd}$. Prove that if $c \neq d$, then their arithmetic mean exceeds their geometric mean. Suggestion: $\sqrt{c}$ and $\sqrt{d}$ are unequal, so $(\sqrt{c} - \sqrt{d})^2$ is positive.

11. Which of the following propositions are true for all real numbers a, b, c, d, and which are false? Give reasons for your answers.

    (i) If $a \neq b$ and $c \neq d$ then $a + c \neq b + d$.

    (ii) If $a \neq b$ then $c + a \neq c + b$.

(iii) If $a \neq b$, $a \neq 0$, $b \neq 0$, then $1/a \neq 1/b$.

(iv) If $a \neq b$ and $c \neq d$, then $ac \neq bd$.

(v) If $a \neq b$ then $a^2 \neq b^2$.

(vi) If $a \neq b$ and $c \neq 0$, then $ac \neq bc$.

12. Which of the following propositions are true, and which false? (Remark: A mathematical proposition is true only if it is universally true, not just in some cases or some circumstances.)

(a) The sum of two positive numbers is non-negative.

(b) The sum of two non-negative numbers is positive.

(c) The sum of a positive number and a non-negative number is positive.

(d) The product of a positive number and a non-negative number is positive.

(e) The product of two positive numbers is non-negative.

(f) The product of two non-negative numbers is positive.

2.2. Absolute Values.

Let x be any real number. The notation $|x|$ stands for "the absolute value of x", and it is defined as follows:

if x is positive or zero, $|x| = x$;

if x is negative, $|x| = -x$.

We give some examples:

$$|3| = 3, \quad |-8| = 8, \quad |-14| = 14,, \quad |0| = 0, \quad |6| = 6.$$

There is another way of defining $|x|$ that amounts to the same thing, namely $|x| = \sqrt{x^2}$. This is the same as the earlier definition because of the convention in mathematics that the $\sqrt{\ }$ symbol always denotes a non-negative value in the real number system. For example we see that

$$\sqrt{(-8)^2} = \sqrt{64} = 8, \quad \text{so} \quad |-8| = \sqrt{(-8)^2}.$$

Notice that $|8| = |-8|$, and in general $|x| = |-x|$.

THEOREM 7. *The absolute value of a product of two real numbers equals the product of their absolute values, i.e., $|xy| = |x| \cdot |y|$.*

PROOF. First we give a direct proof, and then a short, more sophisticated proof. In case x or y is zero, then xy is zero and we see that

$$|xy| = 0, \quad |x| \cdot |y| = 0, \quad \text{so} \quad |xy| = |x| \cdot |y|.$$

There remain the cases where neither x or y is zero. If both are positive, then their product xy is also positive, and we see that

$$|xy| = xy, \quad |x| = x, \quad |y| = y, \quad \text{so} \quad |xy| = |x| \cdot |y|.$$

If both x and y are negative, then xy is positive, and we see that

$$|xy| = xy, \quad |x| = -x, \quad |y| = -y, \text{ so } |xy| = |x| \cdot |y|.$$

Finally we must consider the case where either x or y is positive and the other negative. There is no loss of generality in taking x positive and y negative. Now xy is negative, and it follows that

$$|xy| = -xy, \quad |x| = x, \quad |y| = -y, \quad \text{so} \quad |xy| = |x| \cdot |y|.$$

Now we give a shorter proof of Theorem 7. By using the definition $|x| = \sqrt{x^2}$ we see that

$$|x| = \sqrt{x^2}, \quad |y| = \sqrt{y^2}, \quad |x| \cdot |y| = \sqrt{x^2}\sqrt{y^2} = \sqrt{x^2 y^2} = |xy|.$$

THEOREM 8. *Let* x, y, u, v *be any real numbers satisfying* $|x| < u$, $|y| < v$. *Then these inequalities can be multiplied to give* $|xy| < uv$.

PROOF. Because $|x|$ and $|y|$ are non-negative whatever may be the values of x and y, we can apply Theorem 4 with a, b, c, d replaced by u $|x|$, v, $|y|$, respectively. Thus we conclude that $|x| \cdot |y| < uv$, and from this the present theorem follows by the use of Theorem 7.

A moment's reflection will reveal that such a statement as "x lies strictly between -3 and $+3$" can be written in two ways in mathematical symbolism:

$$-3 < x < 3 \quad \text{and} \quad |x| < 3.$$

This can be conceived pictorially on the real line:

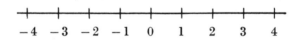

$$\leftarrow \quad \text{set of values of } x \quad \rightarrow$$

Similarly if we wanted to say that x lies strictly between -10^{-5} and 10^{-5}, we could write $|x| < 10^{-5}$. Thus x would be very small numerically. However, degrees of smallness are a relative matter, and so we shall rely on the mathematical symbols to tell the story.

How can we write mathematically that x is (strictly) within 10^{-5}, plus or minus, of the value 3? Using inequalities we could write

$$3 - 10^{-5} < x < 3 + 10^{-5}.$$

By Theorem 2 we can subtract 3 across the series of inequalities to get

$$-10^{-5} < x - 3 < 10^{-5}.$$

Now this can be written $|x - 3| < 10^{-5}$. Since $|x - 3|$ and $|3 - x|$ are the same, this can also be written $|3 - x| < 10^{-5}$.

Thus the symbol $|x-3|$ is a measure of how near x is to 3. Similarly $|x-t|$ is a measure of how near x is to t, when these are regarded as numbers on the real line. More precisely,

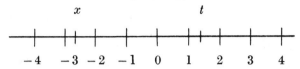

$|x-t|$ is the distance between the points represented by x and t. Here distance is defined in terms of the unit length, which in turn is defined as the length of the line segment from the point 0 to the point 1.

EXAMPLE: What values of x are described by the inequality $|x-5| \leq 2$? Stated in terms of the geometry of the real line, this says that the distance from the point x to the point 5 is at most 2. Hence the inequality denotes the set of all real numbers from $x = 3$ to $x = 7$. This set can also be described by the inequalities $3 \leq x \leq 7$.

For use in questions of maxima and minima in Chapter 4, it will be convenient to have an analysis of such questions as: For what values of x is $x^2 - 5x + 6 > 0$? This inequality can be written as $(x-2)(x-3) > 0$, suggesting the following approach to the question. The expression $(x-2)(x-3)$ is a product of the two factors $x-2$ and $x-3$. These factors may be positive or negative, depending on the value of x. Thus we see that $(x-2)(x-3) > 0$ if and only if

(a) both conditions $x-2 > 0$ and $x-3 > 0$ are satisfied, or

(b) both conditions $x-2 < 0$ and $x-3 < 0$ are satisfied.

Now in part (a) the conditions are the same as $x > 2$ and $x > 3$, and both of these are satisfied if and only if $x > 3$. In part (b) the conditions are $x < 2$ and $x < 3$, and both of these are satisfied if and only if $x < 2$. Thus the answer to the question is this: $x^2 - 5x + 6 > 0$ if and only if x satisfies $x > 3$ or $x < 2$.

Consider another example: For what values of x is $x^2 + 4x - 5 < 0$? This inequality can be written as $(x-1)(x+5) < 0$, and so we conclude that one of the factors $x-1$ and $x+5$ must be positive and the other negative. Hence we require that

(a) both conditions $x-1 < 0$ and $x+5 > 0$ are satisfied, or

(b) both conditions $x-1 > 0$ and $x+5 < 0$ are satisfied.

In part (a) the conditions are $x < 1$ and $x > -5$, both of which are satisfied if and only if $-5 < x < 1$. In part (b) the conditions are $x > 1$ and $x < -5$, and there is no value of x satisfying both of these. Thus the answer to the question is: $x^2 + 4x - 5 < 0$ if and only if $-5 < x < 1$.

Problems

1. Given that a variable x stays strictly between 3 and 7, show that this can be written mathematically in any one of the following ways:
   - (a) $3 < x < 7$
   - (b) $7 > x > 3$
   - (c) $|x-5| < 2$
   - (d) $2 > |x-5|$

2. Given that a variable x stays strictly between 4 and 10, write this mathematically in four ways, analogous to those in Question 1.

3. Given that a variable x stays strictly between 100 and 200, write this mathematically in four ways.

4. Given that a variable x stays strictly between $\frac{1}{2}$ and $-\frac{1}{2}$, write this mathematically in four ways.

5. When a certain thermostat is set at 72, it does not allow the temperature T to vary from this by more than 2 degrees. Write this mathematically in four ways.

6. Given that two real numbers x and y differ by at most 3, write this mathematically in as many ways as you can (not more than eight). Remark: Actually, any inequality can be written in infinitely many ways. For example $x > 4$ can be written $2x > 8$, $3x > 12$, $4x > 16$, $5x > 20$, etc.

7. Given that two real numbers x and y differ by at most ϵ, where ϵ is positive, write this mathematically in as many ways as you can, up to eight.

8. Write each of the following inequalities without absolute value signs, given that ϵ is positive:
   - (a) $|x| < 6$
   - (b) $|x| < \epsilon$
   - (c) $|x-3| < 7$
   - (d) $|x-3| < \epsilon$
   - (e) $|x-3| \leqq 7$
   - (f) $|x-3| \leqq \epsilon$
   - (g) $|x-7| < 3$
   - (h) $|x-3| \leqq 7$

9. Write each of the following inequalities with absolute value signs:
   - (a) $-9 < x < 9$
   - (b) $-9 \leqq x \leqq 9$
   - (c) $14 < x < 30$
   - (d) $12 < x < 20$
   - (e) $-4 < x-3 < 4$
   - (f) $-4 < x-3 < 0$

10. What values of x satisfy both inequalities $x-5 > 0$ and $x+4 > 0$?

11. What values of x satisfy both inequalities $x-7 < 0$ and $x+2 > 0$?

12. What values of x satisfy both inequalities $x-7 < 0$ and $x-9 > 0$?

13. For what values of x is $x^2-7x+6 > 0$?

14. Determine x so that $x^2+7x-8 < 0$.

15. Determine x so that $x^2-x-42 < 0$.

16. For what values of x is $x^2+2x > 15$?

17. Solve the inequality $x^2 > 6x-5$.

18. Determine x so that $x^2 < 3x$.

2.3 Sequences and Limits. In our examination of sample problems from calculus in Chapter 1, we were led in each case into a problem in limits or limiting processes. We now study the problem systematically, confining our attention, however, to cases that will arise in subsequent chapters.

A sequence is an ordered collection of terms, as for example

$$\frac{2}{1}, \frac{3}{2}, \frac{4}{3}, \frac{5}{4}, \frac{6}{5}, \frac{7}{6}, \cdots ,$$

or

$$\frac{1}{2}, \frac{1}{4}, \frac{1}{8}, \frac{1}{16}, \frac{1}{32}, \frac{1}{64}, \cdots ,$$

or

$$0, 1, \ 0, 1, 0, 1, 0, 1 \ldots ,$$

Some sequences tend to limits, other do not. In the three examples of sequences just cited, the first sequence tends to the limit 1, the second sequence to the limit 0, and the third sequence has no limit. Another example is the well-known sequence

$$.3, .33, .333, .3333, .33333, \ldots ,$$

and this has limit $\frac{1}{3}$. The sequence

$$\frac{1}{1}, \frac{1}{2}, \frac{1}{3}, \frac{1}{4}, \frac{1}{5}, \cdots$$

is tending towards the value 0, so the limit of the sequence is 0. Since the nth term of the sequence is $1/n$, we write

$$(1) \qquad\qquad \lim_{n \to \infty} \frac{1}{n} = 0.$$

In words, the limit of $1/n$ as n tends to infinity equals zero.

In the examples given it may have been noted that the symbol n is used to denote a discrete variable, that is, one of the positive integers $n = 1, 2, 3, 4, \ldots$. On the other hand, letters like x and y are customarily used to denote continuous variables. For example, if we write

$$(2) \qquad\qquad \lim_{x \to \infty} \frac{1}{x} = 0,$$

we mean that as x increases indefinitely through real values the limit is zero. Thus in (2) we think of x moving to the right over the positive end of the real line, whereas in (1) the variable n jumps from positive integer to positive integer along the real line. Although the reasoning underlying (1) and (2) is very similar, we make a distinction between these two. The first is called the limit of a sequence, the second the limit of a function.

What we have done thus far is purely descriptive. We now turn to an exact formulation of the idea of a limit. Consider a general infinite sequence of real numbers

$$(3) \qquad\qquad a_1, a_2, a_3, a_4, \ldots$$

whose nth term is a_n. We designate such a sequence briefly by $\{a_n\}$, using braces around the nth term. Now if this sequence is to have limit a, what this means is that the difference $a_n - a$ is tending to zero as n gets larger and larger. That is, as n changes from 1 to 2 to 3 to 4 and so on, the difference $a_n - a$ gets as small as we please, and stays small, for all values of n that are large enough. For instance, we require that $a_n - a$ shall be less than $1/10{,}000{,}000$ for all n beyond some particular value. Furthermore, this must be true not only for $1/10{,}000{,}000$ but for any positive numerical value, as small as we please. To make this precise, we state it as follows.

DEFINITION. *The sequence* (3) *has limit* a *provided that for any given positive number* ϵ, *no matter how small, the inequality*

$$(4) \qquad\qquad |a_n - a| < \epsilon, \quad \text{i.e.,} \quad -\epsilon < a_n - a < \epsilon$$

holds for all but a finite number of terms of the sequence (3).

When this is the case we write

$$\lim_{n \to \infty} a_n = a, \quad \text{or} \quad a_n \to a \quad \text{as} \quad n \to \infty;$$

in words, the limit of a_n as n tends to infinity is a, or a_n tends to a as n tends to infinity.

Note that the effect of the requirement (4) is to make certain that a_n is numerically close to a, at least for large values of n—for example, if ϵ is very small, say $\epsilon = 10^{-20}$, then a_n must be within 10^{-20} of a, except for a finite number of values of n. Furthermore, in order that a sequence may have a limit, the inequalities (4) must hold for $\epsilon = 10^{-50}$, $\epsilon = 10^{-100}$, in fact for any given positive ϵ, not for all values 1, 2, 3, ... of n, but for all but a finite number.

Let us apply the definition to the simple sequence $1/1, 1/2, 1/3, 1/4, \ldots$, and let us test whether our claim that this has limit 0 meets the requirement (4). To be specific, let us take $\epsilon = 1/100$. Then (4) becomes

$$\left|\frac{1}{n} - 0\right| < \frac{1}{100}, \quad \text{i.e.,} \quad -\frac{1}{100} < \frac{1}{n} < \frac{1}{100}.$$

It is clear that these inequalities are satisfied by all terms of the sequence $\{1/n\}$ except the first 100 terms, namely the terms

$$\frac{1}{1}, \frac{1}{2}, \frac{1}{3}, \cdots, \frac{1}{100}.$$

Let us take another value for ϵ, say $\epsilon = 10^{-20}$. Then (4) becomes

$$\left|\frac{1}{n} - 0\right| < 10^{-20}, \quad \text{i.e.,} \quad -\frac{1}{10^{20}} < \frac{1}{n} < \frac{1}{10^{20}}.$$

These inequalities hold except for $n = 1$, $n = 2$, $n = 3$, ..., $n = 10^{20}$, and this is a finite number of exceptions.

The only trouble with taking $\epsilon = 1/100$ and $\epsilon = 10^{-20}$ is that we have verified (4) for just two values of ϵ. Nevertheless these two cases suggest how we can deal with the general value of ϵ. For any given positive ϵ the inequality (4) for the sequence $1/1$, $1/2$, $1/3$, ... takes the form

$$(5) \qquad \left|\frac{1}{n} - 0\right| < \epsilon, \quad \text{i.e.,} \quad -\epsilon < \frac{1}{n} < \epsilon.$$

Now the inequality $-\epsilon < (1/n)$ certainly holds since n and ϵ are positive. Furthermore, $(1/n) < \epsilon$ holds for all values of n satisfying $n > \epsilon^{-1}$, because these two inequalities are equivalent by Theorem 6 of § 2.1. Thus we have established that the sequence $\{1/n\}$ has limit zero.

Not every sequence has a limit. For example, consider the sequence $-1, 1, -1, 1, -1, 1, \ldots$ whose nth term is $(-1)^n$. It is intuitively clear that this sequence has no limit, but we can establish this conclusion analytically in terms of the definition. For suppose there were a limit, say a. Then let the given number ϵ be taken as $\frac{1}{2}$. By (4) the inequalities

$$(6) \qquad |(-1)^n - a| < \tfrac{1}{2}$$

would have to hold for all but a finite number of values of n. Now either $a \geq 0$ or $a < 0$, and we treat these two possibilities separately.

In case $a \geq 0$, then for $n = 1, 3, 5, 7, \ldots$ the absolute value in (6) becomes $|(-1) - a|$. But this is a measure of how near -1 is to a, so we see that $|(-1) - a| \geq 1$, and hence (6) fails to hold for all odd values of n.

In case $a < 0$ we look to the even values of n to establish the result. For $n = 2, 4, 6, 8, \ldots$ the absolute value in (6) becomes $|1-a|$. Thinking of this as a measure of how near 1 is to a, we have $|1-a| > 1$, and so (6) fails to hold for even values of n. Hence the sequence $\{(-1)^n\}$ has no limit.

The definition does not tell us what the limit of a sequence is. That is determined by educated guessing. The definition can be used to test whether the guess, or conjecture, is right, as we tested the limit 0 for the sequence $\{1/n\}$. However, we shall not ordinarily take each sequence to the definition as a test, but rather we shall use some consequences of the definition as our criteria. That is, from the definition we now prove some theorems* which enable us, by starting from certain simple sequences like $\{1/n\}$, to conclude that other more complicated sequences have limits, and also to determine what these limits are.

THEOREM 9.   *Let $\{a_n\}$ be a sequence of non-negative numbers such that $a_n \to 0$ as $n \to \infty$, and let $\{b_n\}$ be a sequence of non-negative numbers satisfying $b_1 \leqq a_1$, $b_2 \leqq a_2$, $b_3 \leqq a_3$, etc. Then $b_n \to 0$ as $n \to \infty$.*

PROOF.   Since the sequence $\{a_n\}$ satisfies (4) with a replaced by 0, then for any positive number ϵ the inequalities

$$-\epsilon < a_n < \epsilon$$

hold for all but a finite number of terms of the sequence. But $-\epsilon < a_n < \epsilon$ implies $-\epsilon < b_n < \epsilon$ because b_n is non-negative, and because $b_n \leqq a_n$. Hence the theorem is proved.

COROLLARY 10.   *As $n \to \infty$, $(1/n) \to 0$, $(1/n^2) \to 0$ and in general $(1/n^k) \to 0$ for any positive integer k.*

PROOF.   We have already proved that $\lim 1/n = 0$, and since by Theorem 6 $(1/n^2) \leqq (1/n)$ we conclude that $(1/n^2) \to 0$ as $n \to \infty$, by Theorem 9. A similar argument applies to $1/n^k$.

We conclude this section with an observation on our definition of limit of a sequence. An alternative definition which is commonly given in books on mathematics (but which we shall not use) is that the sequence (3) has limit a provided that for any given positive number ϵ there is a fixed integer N such that $-\epsilon < a_n - a < \epsilon$ for all values of

---

* Some of the proofs of the theorems on limits in §§ 2.4 and 2.8 might well be omitted at a first reading, especially if these proofs seem obscure or difficult. However, the reader should certainly study the statements of the theorems with care in order to comprehend their meanings.

n exceeding N. Note that this amounts to saying that the inequalities on $a_n - a$ hold for all but a finite number of values of n.

Problems

1. Find the limits (if any) of the following sequences:

(a) $\dfrac{1}{2}, \dfrac{1}{4}, \dfrac{1}{6}, \dfrac{1}{8}, \dfrac{1}{10}, \dfrac{1}{12}, \dots$;

(b) $-\dfrac{1}{2}, -\dfrac{1}{4}, -\dfrac{1}{6}, -\dfrac{1}{8}, -\dfrac{1}{10}, -\dfrac{1}{12}, \dots$;

(c) $\dfrac{3}{1}, \dfrac{4}{2}, \dfrac{5}{3}, \dfrac{6}{4}, \dfrac{7}{5}, \dfrac{8}{6}, \dfrac{9}{7}, \dfrac{10}{8}, \dots$;

(d) $1, \dfrac{1}{2}, 1, \dfrac{1}{3}, 1, \dfrac{1}{4}, 1, \dfrac{1}{5}, 1, \dfrac{1}{6}, 1, \dfrac{1}{7}, \dots$;

(e) $1, \dfrac{1}{2}, 1, \dfrac{2}{3}, 1, \dfrac{3}{4}, 1, \dfrac{4}{5}, 1, \dfrac{5}{6}, 1, \dfrac{6}{7}, \dots$;

(f) $\dfrac{1}{1+1^2}, \dfrac{1}{1+2^2}, \dfrac{1}{1+3^2}, \dfrac{1}{1+4^2}, \dfrac{1}{1+5^2}, \dots$.

2. What is the limit of the sequence $2, 2, 2, 2, \dots$? of the sequence $c, c, c, c, \dots$?

3. Given that the sequence $a_1, a_2, a_3, a_4, \dots$ has limit a, what would you expect to be the limits of the following sequences:

(i) $-a_1, -a_2, -a_3, -a_4, \dots$;

(ii) $1+a_1, 1+a_2, 1+a_3, 1+a_4, \dots$;

(iii) $\frac{1}{2}a_1, \frac{1}{2}a_2, \frac{1}{2}a_3, \frac{1}{2}a_4, \dots$;

(iv) $a_1-a, a_2-a, a_3-a, a_4-a, \dots$.

Give proofs in cases (iii) and (iv).

4. If the nth term of a sequence is $1/(n^2+n)$, what are the first three terms? What is the limit of this sequence?

5. Given that the sequence $a_1, a_2, a_3, a_4, \dots$ has limit a, what are the limits of the sequences

(1) $a_4, a_5, a_6, a_7, a_8, a_9, \dots$;

(2) $a_2, a_4, a_6, a_8, a_{10}, a_{12}, \dots$?

Give a proof in each case.

6. Find the limit of the sequence

$$\frac{1}{1^3}, \frac{1}{2^3}, \frac{1}{3^3}, \frac{1}{4^3}, \frac{1}{5^3}, \dots .$$

*7. Let $\{a_n\}$ and $\{b_n\}$ be sequences with limit zero. Prove that the sequence $\{a_n + b_n\}$ having the terms $a_1 + b_1$, $a_2 + b_2$, $a_3 + b_3$, .. , also has limit zero.

8. Exhibit two sequences $\{a_n\}$ and $\{b_n\}$, neither of which has a limit, but such that the sequence $\{a_n + b_n\}$ has a limit. (By "exhibit a sequence" is meant write or assign specific numerical values for its terms.)

9. Exhibit a sequence $\{a_n\}$ with limit 4, but such that $a_n > 4$ for all terms of the sequence.

10. Exhibit a sequence $\{a_n\}$ with limit 4, but such that $a_n > 4$ if n is even, and $a_n < 4$ if n is odd.

11. Verify that the inequalities (4) in the definition of a limit can be written alternatively as $|a - a_n| < \epsilon$ or $-\epsilon < a - a_n < \epsilon$.

*12. Prove that the sequence .3, .33, .333, .3333, ... has limit $\frac{1}{3}$. Suggestion: Use the formula $a(1 - r^n)/(1 - r)$ for the sum of n terms of the geometric progression a, ar, ar^2, ar^3, ...

2.4 Theorems on Limits. In many cases it is a lot of bother to test a sequence for a limit by using the definition. For example, one of the above problems is to show that .3, .33, .333, ... has limit $\frac{1}{3}$, and, with this done, there is no need to use the ϵ process to establish that the sequences

$$-.3, \ -.33, \ -.333, ...$$

and

$$.6, .66, .666, ...$$

have limits $-\frac{1}{3}$ and $\frac{2}{3}$ respectively. These can be obtained by multiplying the original sequence by -1 and 2, respectively. The general result is as follows.

THEOREM 11. *If c is any constant, and if the sequence a_1, a_2, a_3, ... has limit a, then the sequence ca_1, ca_2, ca_3, ... has limit ca. Stated more briefly, if $\lim a_n = a$, then $\lim ca_n = ca$.*

PROOF. First consider the special case $c = 0$. In this case the sequence $\{ca_n\}$ consists of 0, 0, 0, ..., and the limit is 0, which is the value of ca.

Second, we consider the situation when c is not equal to zero, that is $c \neq 0$. Then $|c|$ is positive, and for any positive ϵ the number $\epsilon/|c|$ is also positive. We apply the definition of limit with $\epsilon/|c|$ as the "given positive number". Thus by (4) the inequality

$$|a_n - a| < \frac{\epsilon}{|c|}$$

holds for all but a finite number of values of n. Multiplying this inequality by $|c|$, and using Theorems 2 and 7, we see that

$$|ca_n - ca| < \epsilon$$

holds for all but a finite number of values of n. Hence the limit of ca_n is ca.

THEOREM 12. *If* $\lim a_n = a$ *and* $\lim b_n = b$, *then* $\lim(a_n + b_n) = a + b$, $\lim(a_n - b_n) = a - b$, *and* $\lim(a_n b_n) = ab$. ALTERNATIVE STATEMENT: *If* $\lim a_n$ *and* $\lim b_n$ *exist, then*

$$\lim(a_n + b_n) = \lim a_n + \lim b_n,$$
$$\lim(a_n - b_n) = \lim a_n - \lim b_n,$$

and

$$\lim(a_n b_n) = (\lim a_n)(\lim b_n).$$

PROOF. *Part* 1. Let ϵ be any positive number. We use $\epsilon/2$ as the "given positive number" in the definition of limit for the sequences $\{a_n\}$ and $\{b_n\}$. Thus by (4) each of the inequalities

$$-(\epsilon/2) < a_n - a < (\epsilon/2) \quad \text{and} \quad -(\epsilon/2) < b_n - b < (\epsilon/2)$$

holds for all but a finite number of values of n. Hence these inequalities on $a_n - a$ and $b_n - b$ hold simultaneously for all but a finite number of values of n. For example, if the inequalities on $a_n - a$ hold for all values of n except $n = 1, 2, 3, 4, 5, 8, 9$, and if the inequalities on $b_n - b$ hold for all values of n except $n = 1, 2, 3, 5, 9, 12$, then the inequalities hold simultaneously for all values of n except $n = 1, 2, 3, 4, 5, 8, 9, 12$. By Theorem 3 we can add these inequalities to get

$$-\epsilon < (a_n + b_n) - (a + b) < \epsilon,$$

which holds for all but a finite number of values of n, and so $\lim(a_n + b_n) = a + b$.

Part 2. By Theorem 11 applied to the sequence $\{b_n\}$ with $c = -1$, we conclude that $\lim(-b_n) = -b$. Then we have, using Part 1,

$$\lim(a_n - b_n) = \lim[a_n + (-b_n)] = \lim a_n + \lim(-b_n) = a - b.$$

Part 3. To prove that the limit of a product of two sequences is equal to the product of the limits of the sequences, we begin with the special case where the limits are zero. That is to say, we prove that if two sequences $\{\alpha_n\}$ and $\{\beta_n\}$ have the properties $\lim \alpha_n = 0$ and $\lim \beta_n = 0$, then $\lim(\alpha_n \beta_n) = 0$. By (4) we conclude that for any positive ϵ the inequalities $|\alpha_n| < \epsilon$ and $|\beta_n| < \epsilon$ hold for all but a finite number of values of n. Using Theorems 4 and 7 we can multiply these inequalities to get $|\alpha_n \beta_n| < \epsilon^2$, and this too holds for all but a finite number of values of n. Now since the whole question of limits centers on small values of ϵ, we may certainly presume that $\epsilon < 1$. Multiplying this inequality by ϵ, we get $\epsilon^2 < \epsilon$, and so we have $|\alpha_n\beta_n| < \epsilon^2 < \epsilon$. It follows that $\lim(\alpha_n\beta_n) = 0$.

Having proved this special case, we return to the general question of the value of $\lim(a_nb_n)$, given that $\lim a_n = a$ and $\lim b_n = b$. Noting that $\lim(a_n - a) = 0$ and $\lim(b_n - b) = 0$, we identify $a_n - a$ and α_n, and similarly $b_n - b$ and β_n. Then we have

$$a_n = a + \alpha_n, \quad b_n = b + \beta_n, \quad a_nb_n = ab + a\beta_n + b\alpha_n + \alpha_n\beta_n.$$

The last equation suggests that we can study $\lim(a_nb_n)$ in the following way:

$$\lim(ab + a\beta_n + b\alpha_n + \alpha_n\beta_n)$$
$$= \lim(ab) + \lim(a\beta_n) + \lim(b\alpha_n) + \lim(\alpha_n\beta_n)$$
$$= ab + a \lim \beta_n + b \lim \alpha_n + 0$$
$$= ab + 0 + 0 + 0 = ab.$$

In these steps we have used part of Theorem 12 already proved, and also Theorem 11. Thus we have proved that $\lim(a_nb_n) = ab$.

COROLLARY 13. *If* $\lim a_n = a$ *and* $\lim(a_n - b_n) = 0$, *then* $\lim b_n = a$.

PROOF. We apply Theorem 12 in the following fashion:

$$\lim b_n = \lim[a_n - (a_n - b_n)] = \lim a_n - \lim(a_n - b_n) = a - 0 = a.$$

THEOREM 14. *Let* c *be a constant and let* $\{a_n\}$ *be a sequence with no term less than* c, *and* $\{b_n\}$ *a sequence with no term greater than* c. *In other words* $a_n \geq c$ *and* $b_n \leq c$ *for all values of* n. *If* $\lim(a_n - b_n) = 0$ *then* $\lim a_n = c$ *and* $\lim b_n = c$.

PROOF. Let ϵ be a given positive quantity. Then the inequalities

$$-\epsilon < a_n - b_n < \epsilon$$

hold for all but a finite number of values of n, by the definition (4) applied to the sequence $\{a_n - b_n\}$. The inequality $a_n - b_n < \epsilon$ can be written in the form

$$(a_n - c) + (c - b_n) < \epsilon.$$

But this implies $a_n - c < \epsilon$ and $c - b_n < \epsilon$ since both $a_n - c$ and $c - b_n$ are non-negative. Hence we get

$$0 \leq a_n - c < \epsilon, \quad \text{and} \quad -\epsilon < a_n - c < \epsilon.$$

Since this holds for all but a finite number of values of n, we conclude that $\lim a_n = c$. Applying Corollary 13, with c now playing the role of a, we also conclude that $\lim b_n = c$.

THEOREM 15. *If no term of the sequence $\{c_n\}$ is positive, and if $\lim c_n = c$, then $c \leqq 0$.*

PROOF. We use an indirect argument. Suppose that $c > 0$. We apply the definition of limit to the sequence $\{c_n\}$, using $c/2$ as the "given positive number". Thus by (4),

$$-(c/2) < c_n - c < (c/2)$$

holds for all but a finite number of terms of the sequence $\{c_n\}$. But to the inequality $-(c/2) < c_n - c$ we can add c by Theorem 2 to get $(c/2) < c_n$. However, $c > 0$, and so $(c/2) > 0$, and thus $c_n > 0$. But this is a contradiction, and hence we conclude that $c \leqq 0$.

THEOREM 16. *If $\lim a_n = a$ and $\lim b_n = b$, and if $a_n \leqq b_n$ holds for $n = 1, 2, 3, \ldots$, then $a \leqq b$.*

PROOF. We see that $\lim(a_n - b_n) = a - b$ by Theorem 12. Applying Theorem 15 with c_n replaced by $a_n - b_n$, we conclude that $a - b \leqq 0$, or $a \leqq b$.

THEOREM 17. *Suppose there are sequences $\{s_n\}$, $\{S_n\}$ and $\{\sigma_n\}$ satisfying $\lim s_n = c$, $\lim S_n = c$ and*

$$s_n \leqq \sigma_n \leqq S_n$$

for $n = 1, 2, 3, 4, \ldots$. Then $\lim \sigma_n = c$.

PROOF. By Theorem 12 we can write

$$\lim(S_n - s_n) = \lim S_n - \lim s_n = c - c = 0.$$

Next we subtract s_n from the given inequalities to get, by Theorem 2,

$$0 \leqq \sigma_n - s_n \leqq S_n - s_n.$$

Applying Theorem 9 with a_n replaced by $S_n - s_n$, and b_n by $\sigma_n - s_n$, we conclude that

$$\lim(\sigma_n - s_n) = 0.$$

This implies that $\lim(s_n - \sigma_n) = 0$, by Theorem 11 with c replaced by -1. Finally we use Corollary 13 to conclude that $\lim \sigma_n = c$.

Problems

1. Evaluate the following limits:

(a) $\lim\limits_{n \to \infty} (2 + 1/n + 1/n^2)$

(b) $\lim\limits_{n \to \infty} \dfrac{4n^2 + n - 5}{n^2}$

(c) $\lim\limits_{n \to \infty} \dfrac{100 + 200n}{n^2}$

(f) $\lim\limits_{n \to \infty} \left(\dfrac{1}{3} + \dfrac{1}{2n} + \dfrac{1}{6n^2} \right)$

(d) $\lim\limits_{n \to \infty} \dfrac{(n-1)(n-2)(n-3)}{n^3}$

(g) $\lim\limits_{n \to \infty} \left(\dfrac{1}{3} - \dfrac{1}{2n} + \dfrac{1}{6n^2} \right)$

(e) $\lim\limits_{n \to \infty} \left(\dfrac{2n-1}{n} \right)^2$

2. Prove that if all terms of a sequence $\{a_n\}$ positive, then the limit (if it exists) of the sequence must be positive or zero. Suggestion: Apply Theorem 15 to the sequence $\{-a_n\}$.

3. Given that the sequence $\{a_n\}$ has limit a, and that the sequence $\{b_n\}$ has limit b, find the limits of the sequences:

(i) $3a_1, 3a_2, 3a_3, 3a_4, 3a_5, 3a_6, \ldots$;

(ii) $b_1 - 2a_1, b_2 - 2a_2, b_3 - 2a_3, b_4 - 2a_4, \ldots$;

(iii) $a_1 - a_2, a_2 - a_3, a_3 - a_4, a_4 - a_5, a_5 - a_6, \ldots$;

(iv) $a_1 + b_2, a_2 + b_3, a_3 + b_4, a_4 + b_5, a_5 + b_6, \ldots$.

*4. Given that a sequence $\{a_n\}$ does have a limit, and that $a_1, a_3, a_5, \ldots$ are all positive but $a_2, a_4, a_6, \ldots$ are all negative, what must the limit be? Exhibit such a sequence.

5. Prove that if $\lim a_n = a$ then $\lim(c + a_n) = c + a$ where c is any constant.

6. Prove that if $\lim a_n = a$, then $\lim(-a_n) = -a$.

7. Prove that if $\lim c_n = c$ and $\lim(q_n - c_n) = 0$, then $\lim q_n = c$.

8. Find $\lim a_n$ and $\lim b_n$, given the information that $\lim(a_n + b_n) = 7$ and $\lim(a_n - b_n) = 3$.

9. If $\lim a_n = a$ and $\lim b_n = b$, what is limit of the sequence

$$\frac{a_1 + b_1}{2}, \quad \frac{a_2 + b_2}{2}, \quad \frac{a_3 + b_3}{2}, \quad \frac{a_4 + b_4}{2}, \ldots \, ?$$

Give a proof.

10. If $\lim a_n = a$ and $\lim b_n = b$, and c and k are constants, evaluate $\lim(ca_n + kb_n)$. Give a proof.

2.5 Functions. In §§ 1.3 and 1.6 we discussed the equation $y = x^2$ and its graph. This equation can be thought of as a rule of correspondence: to every real value assigned to x there corresponds a real value of y. For example, if $x = 5$, then $y = 25$; if $x = -8$, then $y = 64$. This correspondence is an example of a function. In functional notation the equation could be written $f(x) = x^2$, where the symbol $f(x)$ is read "f of x". The numerical examples above can then be written as $f(5) = 25$ and $f(-8) = 64$.

We now drop this special case $f(x) = x^2$ to make some general observations. The word "function" is used in a very restricted sense in this book. In order to avoid a lengthy discussion of the theory of sets, we do not give a general definition of the term. Indeed, for our purposes it is sufficient to say that y is a function of x if whenever x is assigned a numerical value, y is determined uniquely. If we use $f(x)$ in place of y, we can say that a function f is a correspondence which determines exactly one real value $f(x)$ corresponding to each value of x in a certain set of real numbers X. The set X of values of x is called the *domain* of the function; the set of values of $f(x)$ is called the *range* of the function. Notice that we are restricting the domain and the range to be sets of real numbers.

Furthermore, we shall confine our attention to functions for which there is a specific mathematical equation or formula relating x and $f(x)$, for example, $f(x) = x^2$. Also, unless otherwise stated, this equation will specify both the domain and the range of the function: The domain X will consist of all real numbers for which the equation provides a unique real value for $f(x)$; the range is simply the set of all these values of $f(x)$.

For example in the case $f(x) = x^2$, the domain of values of x is the set of all real numbers, and the range of values of $f(x)$ is the set of non-negative real numbers. On the other hand, in the case $f(x) = \sqrt{x}$, the domain is the set of non-negative real numbers, because $\sqrt{x}$ is not real when x is negative. The range of this function is also the set of non-negative real numbers, because of the mathematical convention that $\sqrt{x}$ is positive or zero, never negative. To take a third example, in the case $f(x) = \sqrt{1-x^2}$, the domain is the set of x values satisfying $-1 \leqq x \leqq 1$, and the range is the set of real numbers between 0 and 1; thus $0 \leqq f(x) \leqq 1$.

Because of the restricted class of functions with which we deal, we can specify the function by its equation, and so speak of the function $f(x) = x^2$, or what is the same thing in different notation, the function $y = x^2$. In fact there is need for neither y nor $f(x)$ here; we can speak of the function x^2.

In the same way, we shall speak variously of the graph of the function x^2, or the graph of the function $f(x) = x^2$, of the graph of $y = x^2$, and in each case we mean the same thing, namely the graph illustrated in Figure 6 of § 1.3.

The word "function" is properly attached to the entire correspondence system between the domain and the range, but we will sometimes use the word loosely to refer to the formula for $f(x)$. The sense will be indicated by the context, so that there will be no need to make any fine distinction between the function, f, and the values of the function, $f(x)$.

If we wish to discuss two or more functions simultaneously, we would not call them both $f(x)$, of course. Other notation for functions would be used, such as $g(x)$, $h(x)$, $F(x)$, $G(x)$, etc.

In certain problems in calculus it is convenient to reduce a complicated function to simpler ones. For example the function $y = x^2 + \sin x$ can be separated into $u = x^2$ and $v = \sin x$, with $y = u + v$. As a second example, the function

$$y = x^2\sqrt{1-x}$$

can be written as $y = uv$ with $u = x^2$ and $v = \sqrt{1-x}$. These are simple examples of the addition and multiplication of functions. Another important simplification is the *composition of functions*. In the case

$$y = (x^2 - 3x - 2)^6 - 5(x^2 - 3x - 2)^3$$

for example, we can introduce a new variable u by the equation $u = x^2 - 3x - 2$, and then we write $y = u^6 - 5u^3$. Similarly $y = \sin(3x - 5)$ can be broken up into $y = \sin u$ and $u = 3x - 5$.

But these two illustrations are really examples of the decomposition of functions. Composition is ordinarily formulated in terms of functional notation as follows. If we have

$$f(x) = x^2 + 4x - 7 \quad \text{and} \quad g(x) = 3x + 6,$$

then the composition of f and g (in that order) is

$$f(g(x)) = f(3x + 6) = (3x + 6)^2 + 4(3x + 6) - 7 = 9x^2 + 48x + 53.$$

Observe that $f(3x + 6)$ is evaluated here by replacing x by $3x + 6$ in the equation $f(x) = x^2 + 4x - 7$. The notation $f(g(x))$ is read "f of g of x". The composition of g and f is

$$g(f(x)) = g(x^2 + 4x - 7) = 3(x^2 + 4x - 7) + 6 = 3x^2 + 12x - 15.$$

Here we see that $g(f(x))$ and $f(g(x))$ are different. In special cases it can happen that $f(g(x))$ and $g(f(x))$ are the same function of x, for example if $f(x) = x + 3$ and $g(x) = x - 10$.

As another illustration take the functions

$$f(x) = 2x - 3 \quad \text{and} \quad F(x) = x^2 - x + 9.$$

Then we get

$$f(F(x)) = 2(x^2 - x + 9) - 3 = 2x^2 - 2x + 15,$$

and

$$F(f(x)) = (2x - 3)^2 - (2x - 3) + 9 = 4x^2 - 14x + 21.$$

Problems

1. If the domain of values of x is the set of all real numbers, we can write this symbolically as $-\infty < x < \infty$. Write similar symbolic inequalities to indicate that the domain of x is (a) the set of all positive real numbers; (b) the set of all non-negative real numbers; (c) the set of all negative real numbers.

2. Assuming that the equation specifies the domain and range of the function, give the domain and range of each of the following:

(a) $f(x) = \sqrt{4-x^2}$　　　　　　　(e) $f(x) = 2^{-x}$

(b) $f(x) = \sqrt{4-x^4}$　　　　　　　(f) $f(x) = \sqrt{x-1}$

(c) $f(x) = \sqrt{2}+\sqrt{4-x^2}$　　　　(g) $f(x) = \sqrt{1-x}$

(d) $f(x) = 2^x$　　　　　　　　　　(h) $f(x) = -\sqrt{1-x}$

3. Given $f(x) = 2x^2-3x+4$, find the values of $f(1)$, $f(2)$, $f(3)$, $f(4)$, $f(0)$ and $f(-1)$.

4. Verify that $f(x) = x+3$ and $F(x) = (x^2-9)/(x-3)$ are almost identical functions, the difference being that whereas the domain of $f(x)$ is $-\infty < x < \infty$, the domain of $F(x)$ is $-\infty < x < \infty$ except for the value $x = 3$.

5. Given $f(x) = 3x+7$, find the values of $f(2)$, $f(5)$, $f(c)$, $f(2c)$, $f(2x)$, and $f(2x+6)$. Given also that $g(x) = 2x+6$, find formulas for the functions $f(g(x))$ and $g(f(x))$.

6. Given $f(x) = 2x^4$ and $g(x) = 3x^5$, write formulas for the functions $f(g(x))$ and $g(f(x))$.

7. If $f(x) = 3x+7$ and $f(g(x)) = 6x-20$, find a formula for the function $g(x)$.

8. A linear function is one of the form $f(x) = ax+b$, where a and b are constants with $a \neq 0$. If $g(x)$ is also a linear function, prove that $f(g(x))$ is linear.

9. Let the domain of the function $f(x)$ in the preceding problem be the set of all real numbers. What is the range of the function? Give a proof.

10. Given that $f(x)$ is a polynomial function of degree 2, i.e., $f(x) = ax^2+bx+c$ with $a \neq 0$, determine the coefficients a, b, c from the information $f(0) = 2$, $f(1) = 4$, $f(2) = 16$.

11. Given the function $f(x) = x^2-7$ with domain the set of all real numbers. What is the range of the function?

*12. Let $f(x)$ be a polynomial function of degree 2 as in question 10. Let the domain of $f(x)$ be the set of all real numbers. Prove that, no matter what the numerical values of a, b, c are, the range of the function cannot be the set of all real numbers.

2.6 Trigonometric Functions and Radian Measure. Although it is presumed that the reader has some familiarity with basic trigonometry, we review a few fundamental ideas, especially the radian measure of angles.

Just as there are various units for the measurement of length such as foot, centimeter, and mile, so there are various units for the measurement of angles. The best-known measure of angles is the degree, and its subparts, minutes and seconds. But the degree is obviously an arbitrary measure. A right angle contains 90°, but why not 80° or 100°? A more natural measure is obtained by using in effect lengths of arcs of a circle as the basis for measurement of angles. Consider a circle of radius one, i.e., a so-called *unit circle*, with center at the point C. Choose a point on the circumference, say A, as the fixed point from which the measurement is made. It is customary to take A to the right of the center C as in Figure 2.1. Note that the length of the circumference of a unit

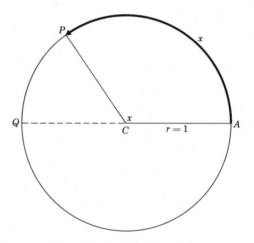

FIG. 2.1. Arc AP of length x.

circle is 2π, because the general formula $2\pi r$ for circumference length reduces to this in the case $r = 1$.

Conceive of the real line, as illustrated in § 2.2, being wrapped around this unit circle, with the zero point of the line placed at A, the positive part of the line going counterclockwise, and the negative part clockwise. In this way each real number x is located at some point on the circle. For example at the point A are the real numbers, 0, 2π, 4π, 6π, ... , and also -2π, -4π, -6π, ... At the point Q diametrically opposite A on the circle are the real numbers π, 3π, 5π, 7π, ... , and also $-\pi$, -3π, -5π, -7π, ...

Suppose that a given real number x is located at the point P on the circle. This is illustrated in Figure 2.1 with a value of x between 0 and π. Note that x is the length of the arc AP. Then the radian measure of the angle ACP (subtended at the center of the circle by the arc AP) is defined to be x. For example if we take x to be $\pi/2$, then the corresponding point P would be located at the top of the circle, so $\pi/2$ radians is the same as 90°. If we take x to be π, then P would be located diametrically opposite A at the position Q in Figure 2.1, so that π radians is the same as 180°. This suggests a simple ratio: for any angle with radian measure x, but with degree measure say α, the ratio x/π is the same as the ratio $\alpha/180$; thus

$$\frac{x}{\pi} = \frac{\alpha}{180} \quad or \quad x = \frac{\pi\alpha}{180}.$$

If $\alpha = 60°$ for instance, then $x = \pi/3$.

The trigonometric values can be written in degree measure or radian measure: either $\sin 60°$ or $\sin \pi/3$; either $\cos 90°$ or $\cos \pi/2$. But whenever we write an equation like $y = \sin x$ or $f(x) = \sin x$ representing a trigonometric function, the angle x is always to be understood in radian measure. The reason for this is that it gives $\sin x$, $\cos x$, etc., as functions of a real variable x, thus giving simpler and more natural results in calculus.

Because of the way the real line was wrapped around the unit circle in the definition above it follows that

$$\sin 0 = \sin 2\pi = \sin 4\pi = \sin 6\pi = \ldots$$
$$= \sin(-2\pi) = \sin(-4\pi) = \sin(-6\pi) = \ldots .$$

In fact for any real number x we can write

$$\sin x = \sin(x+2\pi) = \sin(x+4\pi) = \sin(x+6\pi) = \ldots .$$

These results are included in the more general identities

$$\sin x = \sin(x+2k\pi), \quad \cos x = \cos(x+2k\pi),$$

where k is any integer, positive, negative, or zero.

Here is a brief list of commonly used trigonometric values, with angles in radian measure:

	0	$\dfrac{\pi}{6}$	$\dfrac{\pi}{4}$	$\dfrac{\pi}{3}$	$\dfrac{\pi}{2}$	$\dfrac{2\pi}{3}$	$\dfrac{3\pi}{4}$	$\dfrac{5\pi}{6}$	π
sin	0	$\dfrac{1}{2}$	$\dfrac{\sqrt{2}}{2}$	$\dfrac{\sqrt{3}}{2}$	1	$\dfrac{\sqrt{3}}{2}$	$\dfrac{\sqrt{2}}{2}$	$\dfrac{1}{2}$	0
cos	1	$\dfrac{\sqrt{3}}{2}$	$\dfrac{\sqrt{2}}{2}$	$\dfrac{1}{2}$	0	$-\dfrac{1}{2}$	$-\dfrac{\sqrt{2}}{2}$	$-\dfrac{\sqrt{3}}{2}$	-1
tan	0	$\dfrac{\sqrt{3}}{3}$	1	$\sqrt{3}$	$-$	$-\sqrt{3}$	-1	$-\dfrac{\sqrt{3}}{3}$	0

For convenience we also give a few standard identities:

$$\tan x = \frac{\sin x}{\cos x}, \quad \cot x = \frac{\cos x}{\sin x}, \quad \sec x = \frac{1}{\cos x},$$

$$\csc x = \frac{1}{\sin x}, \quad \sin^2 x + \cos^2 x = 1,$$

$$\sin (x \pm y) = \sin x \cos y \pm \cos x \sin y,$$

$$\cos (x \pm y) = \cos x \cos y \mp \sin x \sin y.$$

Each of the last two is two equations, one with the upper signs matched, and one with the lower.

What we have done, then, is to define the radian measure of an angle as the length of the arc of a unit circle subtending that angle at the center. This definition is based on the concept of arc length, which is taken here as intuitively clear, although in actuality it is itself a question requiring considerable analysis.

Problems

Using the identities given in the text, prove the following:

1. $\sin 2x = 2 \sin x \cos x$.
2. $\cos 2x = \cos^2 x - \sin^2 x = 2 \cos^2 x - 1 = 1 - 2 \sin^2 x$.
3. $\cos x = 1 - 2 \sin^2(x/2)$.
4. $2 \sin x \sin y = \cos(x-y) - \cos(x+y)$.
5. $\sin A - \sin B = 2 \sin(A-B/2) \cos(A+B/2)$. Suggestion: Use the substitution $A = x+y$ and $B = x-y$.
6. Extend the table of values for $\sin x$, $\cos x$, and $\tan x$ given in the text to the following: $x = 7\pi/6, 5\pi/4, 4\pi/3, 3\pi/2, 5\pi/3, 7\pi/4, 11\pi/6, 2\pi$.
7. How many degrees are there in 1 radian? in 5 radians? in x radians? (Leave answers in terms of π).
8. How many radians are there in 1 degree? in 5 degrees? in y degrees? (Leave answers in terms of π).
9. Prove that the radian measure of a given angle is equal to twice the area of the sector of a unit circle having the given angle at the center. (A unit circle is a circle with radius unity.)
10. If a wheel is turning at a rate of three revolutions per second, what is the equivalent rate in radians per second?
11. Prove that in any circle, one radian is the size of the angle subtended at the center by an arc equal in length to the radius.
12. What is the size in radian measure of the angle subtended at the center of a circle by a chord equal in length to the radius?
13. Divide the trigonometric identity $\sin^2 x + \cos^2 x = 1$ first by $\sin^2 x$, second by $\cos^2 x$, to get two other identities.
14. What are the range and domain of the function $f(x) = \sin x$? of the function $g(x) = \cos x$?

2.7 The Limit of a Function. In § 1.3 we discussed the limit of a special function, namely

$$(7) \qquad \lim_{x \to 3} \frac{x^2 - 9}{x - 3} = 6.$$

Before giving a precise definition of the limit of a function, we inquire a little further from an intuitive standpoint. Note that the function in (7) above is not defined at $x = 3$; the domain of the function $(x^2 - 9)/(x - 3)$ is the set of all real numbers except $x = 3$. In case a function is defined for a specific value of x, the limit of the function and the value of the function are frequently the same, as in the cases

$$\lim_{x \to 0}(x^2 + 4) = 4, \quad \lim_{x \to 5} \frac{x^2 - 9}{x - 3} = 8, \quad \lim_{x \to 8}(x^2 - 6x) = 16.$$

Next we turn to a limit which will be of great importance in Chapter 4, namely

$$(8) \qquad \lim_{\theta \to 0} \frac{\sin \theta}{\theta};$$

in words, the limit of $(\sin \theta)/\theta$ as θ approaches 0. The use of θ in place of the variable x is of no significance here. We might just as well inquire about

$$\lim_{x \to 0} \frac{\sin x}{x}.$$

Now $\sin 0 = 0$, so at $\theta = 0$ the function $(\sin \theta)/\theta$ has the "value" $0/0$. But this is no value at all, and so the function $(\sin \theta)/\theta$ is not defined at $\theta = 0$. The domain of the function is the entire set of real numbers except $\theta = 0$.

Why do we say that $0/0$ has no meaning? One way to answer this is to recall the relation of a fraction to an equation. The fraction $54/6$ denotes the solution of the equation $6x = 54$, namely, the solution $x = 9$. Similarly $35/7$ is the solution of the equation $7x = 35$, namely, $x = 5$. But if in a similar way we try to evaluate $0/0$ as the solution of $0x = 0$, we run into a difficulty. For the product $0x$ has the value 0 no matter what number is substituted for x. In other words every real number is a solution of $0x = 0$. Hence $0/0$ can have no meaning.

Let us return to the limit problem (8), and make a brief table of values of $(\sin \theta)/\theta$ as θ tends toward 0:

$$\frac{\sin .1}{.1} = .998 \ 334 \ 166$$

$$\frac{\sin .01}{.01} = .999\ 983\ 333$$

$$\frac{\sin .001}{.001} = .999\ 999\ 833$$

$$\frac{\sin .0001}{.0001} = .999\ 999\ 998$$

(accuracy to 9 places of decimals). These cases suggest that

$$\lim_{\theta \to 0}(\sin \theta)/\theta = 1,$$

and this we now confirm. Consider a sector of a circle of radius 1, with angle θ at the center C. Let θ subtend an arc AB on the circumference. As in the diagram, Figure 2.2, we draw a perpendicular from B to CA, intersecting CA at D. Also we draw a tangent to the circle at A, intersecting the extension of CB at E. The following calculations are made readily:

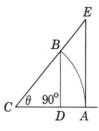

Fig. 2.2

$$\text{radius of circle} = CA = CB = 1,$$

$$\sin \theta = \frac{BD}{BC} = \frac{BD}{1}, \quad BD = \sin \theta,$$

$$\cos \theta = \frac{CD}{BC} = \frac{CD}{1}, \quad CD = \cos \theta,$$

$$\tan \theta = \frac{EA}{CA} = \frac{EA}{1}, \quad EA = \tan \theta,$$

area of triangle $CBD = \frac{1}{2}(CD)(BD) = \frac{1}{2}\cos \theta \sin \theta,$
area of triangle $CAE = \frac{1}{2}(CA)(EA) = \frac{1}{2}(1)(\tan \theta) = \frac{1}{2}\tan \theta.$

The area of the entire circle (of which only the arc AB is shown in Figure 2.2) is $\pi \cdot 1^2$ or π. The area of the sector CAB is in proportion to the angle at the center. That is, the sector subtends an angle θ at the center, whereas the entire circle subtends an angle 2π. Hence the area of the sector CAB is to the area of the whole circle as θ is to 2π, and so

$$\text{area of sector CAB} = \frac{\theta}{2\pi}(\pi) = \frac{\theta}{2}.$$

Next we see that

area of triangle CBD < area of sector CAB < area of triangle CAE,

or

$$\frac{1}{2}\cos\theta\sin\theta < \frac{\theta}{2} < \frac{1}{2}\tan\theta$$

Now we are considering small positive values of θ, so $2/(\sin\theta)$ is positive, and we can use it as a multiplier in accordance with Theorem 2 to get

$$\cos\theta < \frac{\theta}{\sin\theta} < \frac{1}{\cos\theta}.$$

If we take reciprocals and use Theorem 6, we obtain

(9)
$$\frac{1}{\cos\theta} > \frac{\sin\theta}{\theta} > \cos\theta.$$

Now if θ is a small angle, $\cos\theta < 1$ and $1/(\cos\theta) > 1$, and as θ approaches 0, both $\cos\theta$ and its reciprocal tend towards 1. Thus, as θ tends to 0, we see by formula (9) that $(\sin\theta)/\theta$ is caught between two values that are tending to 1. A similar argument applies to $\theta/(\sin\theta)$ in the inequalities preceding (9), and so we conclude that

(10)
$$\lim_{\theta\to 0}\frac{\sin\theta}{\theta} = 1, \quad \lim_{\theta\to 0}\frac{\theta}{\sin\theta} = 1.$$

It is unfortunate in a sense that this limit should equal 1, because it suggests that any limit of the form 0/0 is equal to 1. If we set $\theta = 0$ in the fraction $\sin\theta/\theta$ we get the meaningless symbol 0/0, which suggests the value 1 by analogy to such cases as 7/7, 5/5, 2/2. The point here is that

$$a/a = 1 \text{ for all values of } a \text{ except } a = 0.$$

In the set of problems at the end of § 2.8, there are examples of functions which, although they have the form 0/0 at $\theta = 0$, have limits that are different from 1 as θ tends to 0.

2.8 The Definition of the Limit of a Function. The result (10) that we have just obtained rests on rather shaky ground, because we have not yet given any definition of the limit of a function. The definition is not very different from that of the limit of a sequence in § 2.3. In analogy to (4), for example, we would expect a function $f(x)$ to be near the limit, say a, and so we would require

(11)
$$|f(x)-a| < \epsilon, \quad \text{i.e.,} \quad -\epsilon < f(x)-a < \epsilon.$$

DEFINITION. *A function $f(x)$ is said to have the limit a as x tends to 0 provided that to any given positive number ϵ, there corresponds a positive number δ such that the inequalities* (11) *hold for all values of x in the domain of $f(x)$ satisfying* $0 < |x| < \delta$.

Stated informally, this says that $f(x)$ lies as close to a as we please, say within ϵ of a, provided x is close to 0, specifically within δ of 0. For any positive ϵ, however small, a positive number δ must exist for which the conditions are satisfied. And when the conditions are satisfied we write

$$\lim_{x \to 0} f(x) = a.$$

Another way of writing this is

$$f(x) \to a \quad \text{as} \quad x \to 0;$$

in words, $f(x)$ tends to a as x tends to 0. Figure 2.3 provides a pictorial representation of the definition.

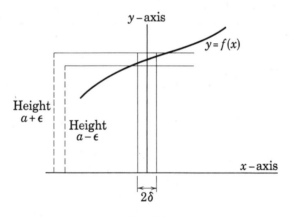

FIG. 2.3

Given any horizontal band of width 2ϵ, bounded by $y = a + \epsilon$ and $y = a - \epsilon$, there exists a vertical band of width 2δ (with the y-axis in the center of the band) so that the graph of the function $f(x)$ falls entirely inside the 2ϵ band for values of x in the 2δ band (except $x = 0$). One reason for making an exception of the $x = 0$ value can be seen from the example of § 2.7, $\lim(\sin x)/x$.

This definition has been confined to the case in which the variable x tends to zero because this is the form in which limits arise in differential calculus. In the next section we give the definition of the limit of a function as x tends to any numerical value.

Although Figure 2.3 suggests that the domain of $f(x)$ is presumed to include all values of x near zero *on both sides of zero*, and although this will in general be the case for the functions we deal with, nevertheless we also want to admit functions like $f(x) = \sqrt{x}$ whose domains include values of x on one side of zero only. So in the case of the function $\sqrt{x}$ we confine attention to positive values of x.

The definition does not require that (11) hold in case $x = 0$. This omission of $x = 0$ is not to be interpreted as meaning that (11) is false when $x = 0$. It means that what happens to $f(x)$ at $x = 0$ is irrelevant; (11) may or may not be satisfied when $x = 0$; indeed $f(x)$ need not be defined at $x = 0$. The latter situation will be the most common occurrence in our use of the limit of a function; that is to say, in most cases the domain of $f(x)$ will not include $x = 0$.

Let us take another look at the result (10) in § 2.7 in the light of the above definition. By rewriting (9) with the inequalities reversed ($a < b < c$ instead of $c > b > a$) and with 1 subtracted from each expression, we have

$$(12) \qquad \cos\theta - 1 < \frac{\sin\theta}{\theta} - 1 < \frac{1}{\cos\theta} - 1.$$

But since we are considering values of θ near 0 but not equal to 0 we know that $\cos\theta$ is near 1, and so we can presume that $\cos\theta > 1/2$. Applying Theorem 6 of § 2.1 we get

$$\frac{1}{\cos\theta} < 2,$$

and so

$$\frac{1}{\cos\theta} - 1 = \frac{1-\cos\theta}{\cos\theta} = \frac{1}{\cos\theta}(1-\cos\theta) < 2(1-\cos\theta).$$

Hence using Theorem 1 of § 2.1 we can rewrite (12) as

$$(13) \qquad -(1-\cos\theta) < \frac{\sin\theta}{\theta} - 1 < 2(1-\cos\theta).$$

This form is beginning to fit the pattern of inequalities (11) where we now have θ in place of x, $(\sin\theta)/\theta$ in place of $f(x)$, and 1 in place of a. The question now is, can $1-\cos\theta$ and $2(1-\cos\theta)$ be made smaller than any given ϵ if we take θ sufficiently close to 0? This follows from the graph of $\cos\theta$ in the vicinity of $\theta = 0$, as in Figure 2.4.

There is one final point to be
made. The entire analysis leading up to inequalities (9) was based
on positive values of θ. But in the
definition of the limit of a
function, the inequalities (11) must
be satisfied for both positive and
negative values of x (or θ, or what-

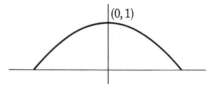

FIG. 2.4   Portion of the graph of cos θ.

ever symbol is appropriate) whenever the domain of the function extends
to both positive and negative values. This point is easily taken care
of, because not only is cos θ symmetric about $\theta = 0$ as shown in Figure
2.4, but also (sin θ)/θ has the same symmetry property:

$$\frac{\sin(-\theta)}{-\theta} = \frac{-\sin\theta}{-\theta} = \frac{\sin\theta}{\theta}, \quad \text{analogous to} \quad \cos(-\theta) = \cos\theta.$$

Consequently the inequalities (13) hold for both positive and negative
values of θ in the vicinity of 0.

The definition of the limit of a function, like the definition of the
limit of a sequence in § 2.3, is not used to find limits nor even very
often to verify conjectured limits. Rather it is used to make the limit
concept mathematically precise and to prove theorems that can be
effectively used to compute various limits. We turn now to theorems of
this kind.

THEOREM 18.   *If* lim $f(x) = a$ *as* x *tends to* 0, *then* lim $cf(x)$
$= c \cdot \lim f(x) = ca$ *for any constant* c.

PROOF.   In case $c = 0$, then $cf(x) = 0$ and $ca = 0$, and the result is
obvious.

Next we treat the case $c = -1$. Since the central idea in the mean-
ing of lim $f(x) = a$ is concerned with $|f(x)-a|$, and since

$$|f(x)-a| = |-f(x)-(-a)|$$

it follows that $\lim(-f(x)) = -a$.

Next let c be positive. For any given positive ϵ, we use the definition
of limit of a function with ϵ/c now playing the role of ϵ. Thus $f(x)$ is
within ϵ/c of a, provided x is sufficiently close to 0, say $0 < |x| < \delta_1$;

$$-\frac{\epsilon}{c} < f(x)-a < \frac{\epsilon}{c} \quad \text{for} \quad 0 < |x| < \delta_1.$$

Multiplying the inequalities by c (permissible by Theorem 2 of § 2.1) we get

$$-\epsilon < cf(x) - ca < \epsilon \quad \text{for} \quad 0 < |x| < \delta_1.$$

and so the theorem holds for any positive value of c.

Finally, for any negative value of c, we write $c = -|c|$, and we apply the previous cases to get

$$\lim cf(x) = \lim[-|c|f(x)] = -\lim[|c|f(x)]$$
$$= -|c|\lim f(x) = -|c|a = ca.$$

All cases have been handled, and the theorem is proved.

Now we prove that the limit of a sum, difference, or product of two functions is the sum, difference, or product of their limits.

THEOREM 19. *If* $\lim f(x) = a$ *and* $\lim g(x) = b$ *as x tends to 0, then* $\lim[f(x) + g(x)] = a + b$ *and* $\lim[f(x) - g(x)] = a - b$.

PROOF. Let ϵ be any given positive number. We apply the definition of limit to both $f(x)$ and $g(x)$ with $\epsilon/2$ now playing the role of ϵ. Hence there exist positive numbers δ_1 and δ_2 such that

$$-\epsilon/2 < f(x) - a < \epsilon/2 \quad \text{for} \quad 0 < |x| < \delta_1,$$

and

$$-\epsilon/2 < g(x) - b < \epsilon/2 \quad \text{for} \quad 0 < |x| < \delta_2.$$

We can add these inequalities, by Theorem 3 of § 2.1, and so we get

$$-\epsilon < f(x) + g(x) - (a + b) < \epsilon \quad \text{for} \quad 0 < |x| < \delta,$$

provided δ is the smaller of δ_1 and δ_2. Hence $\lim(f(x) + g(x)) = a + b$.

In the case $f(x) - g(x)$ we use what we have already proved along with Theorem 18 in the case $c = -1$, thus

$$\lim[f(x) - g(x)] = \lim[f(x) + (-g(x))] = \lim f(x) + \lim(-g(x))$$
$$= \lim f(x) - \lim g(x) = a - b.$$

THEOREM 20. *If* $\lim f(x) = a$ *and* $\lim g(x) = b$ *as x tends to 0, then* $\lim[f(x)g(x)] = \lim f(x) \cdot \lim g(x) = ab$.

PROOF. First we prove the theorem in the special case when $a = 0$ and $b = 0$. So let there be two functions $F(x)$ and $G(x)$ such that $\lim F(x) = 0$ and $\lim G(x) = 0$ as x tends to 0. For any given positive ϵ we apply the definition of limit with $\sqrt{\epsilon}$ playing the role of ϵ:

$$|F(x)| < \sqrt{\epsilon} \quad \text{for} \quad 0 < |x| < \delta_1,$$

and

$$|G(x)| < \sqrt{\epsilon} \quad \text{for} \quad 0 < |x| < \delta_2.$$

We can multiply the inequalities by Theorem 8, and so we have

$$|F(x)G(x)| < \epsilon \quad \text{for} \quad 0 < |x| < \delta,$$

provided δ is the smaller of δ_1 and δ_2. Hence $\lim[F(x)G(x)] = 0$.

Turning now to the general case as described in the theorem, we define $F(x)$ and $G(x)$ as

$$F(x) = f(x) - a, \qquad G(x) = g(x) - b,$$

so that

$$\lim F(x) = \lim[f(x) - a] = \lim f(x) - \lim a = a - a = 0,$$

and

$$\lim G(x) = \lim[g(x) - b] = \lim g(x) - \lim b = b - b = 0.$$

Hence by the first part of the proof we can conclude that as x tends to zero,

$$\begin{aligned}
\lim[f(x)g(x)] &= \lim[\{F(x) + a\}\{G(x) + b\}] \\
&= \lim[F(x)G(x) + aG(x) + bF(x) + ab] \\
&= \lim F(x)G(x) + \lim aG(x) + \lim bF(x) + \lim ab \\
&= 0 + a \cdot \lim G(x) + b \cdot \lim F(x) + ab \\
&= 0 + 0 + 0 + ab = ab.
\end{aligned}$$

THEOREM 21. *If $\lim g(x) = a$ as x tends to 0, and if $a \neq 0$, then $\lim 1/g(x) = 1/a$.*

PROOF. First we establish this in case $a = 1$. Consider a function $F(x)$ such that $\lim F(x) = 1$ as x tends to 0. We apply the definition of limit with $\epsilon/2$ in place of ϵ, so that

$$(14) \qquad |F(x) - 1| < \epsilon/2 \quad \text{for} \quad 0 < |x| < \delta.$$

Since (14) is a technical way of stating that $F(x)$ is close to 1 when x is close to 0, we may presume that $F(x) > 1/2$ for the values of x under discussion. By Theorem 6 of § 2.1, this implies that $\{F(x)\}^{-1} < 2$, and by Theorem 4 of § 2.1 we can multiply this into (14) to get

$$\{F(x)\}^{-1} \cdot |F(x) - 1| < \epsilon, \quad \left|1 - \frac{1}{F(x)}\right| < \epsilon, \quad \text{for} \quad 0 < |x| < \delta.$$

Hence we conclude that $\lim 1/F(x) = 1$.

To prove Theorem 21 in the general case, we note that $\lim g(x)/a = 1$ by Theorem 18. Hence we can apply the result of the preceding paragraph, with $F(x)$ replaced by $g(x)/a$, and we conclude that

$$\lim\left\{\frac{g(x)}{a}\right\}^{-1} = 1, \quad \lim\frac{a}{g(x)} = 1.$$

By Theorem 18 we can multiply this by $1/a$ to get $\lim 1/g(x) = 1/a$, and the proof of Theorem 21 is complete.

As an illustration of Theorem 21, note that by its use we could have deduced either one of the results (10) from the other, instead of proving them both.

In most problems limits are evaluated not by starting from the definition itself but by using the theorems on limits. However, certain basic limits must be known to get the process started. So for use in the problems we establish three simple limits:

$$\lim_{x \to 0} x = 0, \quad \lim_{x \to 0} \sin x = 0, \quad \lim_{x \to 0} \cos x = 1.$$

For the first of these we look at the definition of limit with $f(x)$ replaced by x. We must prove that for any given positive number ϵ there is a corresponding positive number δ such that $-\epsilon < x - 0 < \epsilon$ holds for all values of x satisfying $-\delta < x < \delta$, omitting $x = 0$ from consideration. This situation is easy to analyze because we can take δ to be exactly the same as ϵ, thus $\delta = \epsilon$.

As to $\lim \sin x$, it is awkward (and not easy) to use the definition, so we apply Theorem 20 with $f(x)$ and $g(x)$ replaced by x and $(\sin x)/x$. Thus we get

$$\lim_{x \to 0} \sin x = \lim_{x \to 0} x \cdot \lim_{x \to 0} \frac{\sin x}{x} = 0 \cdot 1 = 0.$$

Turning to $\lim \cos x$, we first extend what we have just proved by noting that $x/2$ tends to zero as x does, and so

$$\lim_{x \to 0} \sin \frac{x}{2} = 0 \quad \text{and} \quad \lim_{x \to 0} \sin^2 \frac{x}{2} = 0,$$

where the second result is again an application of Theorem 20 with both $f(x)$ and $g(x)$ replaced by $\sin x/2$. Recalling the trigonometric identity $\cos x = 1 - 2 \sin^2 x/2$, we use Theorem 19 to get

$$\lim_{x \to 0} \cos x = \lim_{x \to 0} \left(1 - 2 \sin^2 \frac{x}{2}\right) = \lim_{x \to 0} 1 - \lim_{x \to 0} 2 \sin^2 \frac{x}{2} = 1 - 0 = 1.$$

Problems

1. Evaluate

$$\lim_{\theta \to 0} \frac{\sin 2\theta}{2\theta}.$$

2. Evaluate

$$\lim_{\theta \to 0} \frac{\sin 2\theta}{\theta}.$$

Suggestion: Write

$$\frac{\sin 2\theta}{\theta} = 2 \frac{\sin 2\theta}{2\theta},$$

or use the identity $\sin 2\theta = 2 \sin \theta \cos \theta$.

3. Evaluate

$$\lim_{\theta \to 0} \frac{\sin 3\theta}{3\theta} \quad \text{and} \quad \lim_{\theta \to 0} \frac{\sin 3\theta}{\theta}.$$

4. Evaluate

$$\lim_{x \to 0} \frac{\sin x/2}{x}.$$

5. Evaluate

$$\lim_{x \to 0} \frac{1 - \cos x}{x}.$$

Suggestion: Multiply by

$$\frac{1 + \cos x}{1 + \cos x}.$$

6. Evaluate

$$\lim_{v \to 0} \frac{\tan v}{v}.$$

7. Prove that

$$\lim_{x \to 0} x^2 = 0.$$

8. Evaluate the following limits:

(a) $\displaystyle \lim_{x \to 0} \frac{x^2 - x}{x}$

(b) $\displaystyle \lim_{x \to 0} \frac{\sin^2 x}{x \cos x}$

(c) $\displaystyle \lim_{x \to 0} \frac{x^3 + 4x}{5x}$

(d) $\displaystyle \lim_{x \to 0} \frac{\sin^2 x}{5x^2}$

(e) $\displaystyle \lim_{x \to 0} \frac{x^2 - 2x}{x}$

(f) $\displaystyle \lim_{x \to 0} \frac{7x^2 + 4 \sin x}{3x}$

9. Find the numerical values of the following limits:

(a) $\displaystyle\lim_{\theta \to 0} \frac{3\theta + 2\sin\theta}{\theta}$

(c) $\displaystyle\lim_{\theta \to 0} \frac{2\theta}{\theta + \tan\theta}$

(b) $\displaystyle\lim_{\theta \to 0} \frac{3\theta}{\theta + 2\sin\theta}$

(d) $\displaystyle\lim_{\theta \to 0} \frac{2\theta + 3\cos\theta}{\sin\theta + \cos\theta}$

10. Evaluate

$$\lim_{x \to 0} \frac{2\sin x + 3\sin^2 x}{3x + 2x^2}.$$

*11. Given that as x tends to 0, $\lim F(x) = a$ and $\lim G(x) = b \neq 0$, prove that $\lim F(x)/G(x) = a/b$.

2.9 Continuous Functions. The concept of a continuous function is widely used in mathematics, and it is largely for this reason that we define the term here. We will not have much occasion to use the idea in this book because in working out a brief development of calculus it is more convenient to work with other classes of functions.

The definition of limit of a function in the preceding section was restricted to the case "x tends to 0". This admits the rather obvious generalization:

DEFINITION. *A function $f(x)$ is said to have the limit a as x tends to b, written*

$$\lim_{x \to b} f(x) = a,$$

if for any given positive ϵ there exists a corresponding positive δ such that the inequality

$$|f(x) - a| < \epsilon, \quad \text{i.e.,} \quad -\epsilon < f(x) - a < \epsilon$$

holds for all x in the domain of $f(x)$ satisfying $0 < |x - b| < \delta$.

In short, $f(x)$ stays within ϵ of a as long as x is within δ of b. Now we can define the notion of a continuous function.

DEFINITION. *A function $f(x)$ is continuous at $x = b$ if as x tends to b, $f(x)$ tends to $f(b)$, i.e.,*

$$\lim_{x \to b} f(x) = f(b).$$

A function is continuous over an interval if it is continuous at each point in the interval.

What this says is that the function $f(x)$ has a value at $x = b$ which is in harmony with the trend of values of the function as x approaches b.

Another informal way of thinking of a continuous function $f(x)$ is this: that a small change in x produces only a small change in $f(x)$. The definition gives precision to such vague statements. One can think intuitively of a continuous function as one whose graph has no jumps and no breaks. But such a rough formulation, whatever its descriptive value, has no mathematical value because its very imprecision prevents any careful analysis. "No jumps, no breaks"—no theorems!

In order that a function $f(x)$ be continuous at $x = b$, it is necessary that the domain of definition of the function include the value $x = b$; in other words it is necessary that $f(b)$ exist. However, it is not

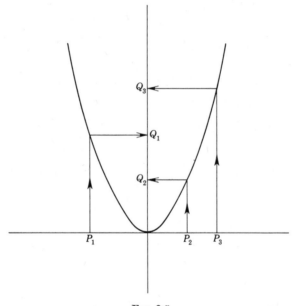

FIG. 2.5

necessary that the function be defined both for values of x on both sides of b: one side will do. For example, the function $y = \sqrt{x}$ with domain $x \geqq 0$ is continuous at $x = 0$ even though the function is not defined for negative values of x. We write

$$\lim_{x \to 0} \sqrt{x} = 0,$$

with the understanding that the limit is taken with positive values of x only.

There is a simple geometric interpretation of this definition, as follows. First observe that any function $f(x)$ can be thought of as a mapping of points on the x-axis onto points on the $f(x)$-axis, or equivalently, the y-axis. For example, consider the function $f(x) = x^2$. We draw the graph of $y = x^2$ in the usual fashion, and then from any point on the x-axis (such as P_1, P_2, P_3 in Figure 2.5) we move vertically to the curve

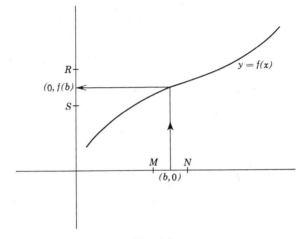

Fig. 2.6

and thence horizontally to get to the corresponding point on the y-axis (such as Q_1, Q_2, Q_3, respectively). If P_3 has coordinates $(2, 0)$ for example, then Q_3 has coordinates $(0, 4)$. More generally, for any function $f(x)$ the point $(b, 0)$ on the x-axis corresponds to the point $(0, f(b))$ on the y-axis. Now $f(x)$ is continuous at $x = b$ if the following condition is satisfied. Let R and S be any two given points on the y-axis equally spaced above and below the point $(0, f(b))$. For any two such points it must be possible to find points M and N on the x-axis, equally spaced to the left and right of $(b, 0)$, so that if any point P is selected on the line segment MN the mapping $f(x)$ carries P into a corresponding point Q on the y-axis lying between R and S. (More accurately, this condition need be satisfied only by points P in MN having x coordinates in the domain of the function $f(x)$.)

Problems

1. Prove that the function $f(x) = x$ is continuous at every real number.
2. Given that $f(x)$ and $g(x)$ are continuous functions at $x = 0$, prove that $f(x) + g(x)$, $f(x) - g(x)$, $cf(x)$, and $f(x)g(x)$ are continuous functions at $x = 0$. Suggestion: Use the theorems of § 2.8.

3. If $f(x)$ is a continuous function at $x = 0$, under what circumstances is $1/f(x)$ a continuous function at $x = 0$?

4. Verify partially that $\lim x^2 = 0$ as x tends to zero by finding a value of δ that will suffice if $\epsilon = 1/1000$.

5. Verify partially that $\lim 1/x = 1/3$ as x tends to 3 by finding a value of δ that will suffice if $\epsilon = 1/100$.

6. If

$$\lim_{x-b} f(x) = k,$$

prove that

$$\lim_{x \to b} cf(x) = ck.$$

7. Prove that the functions $\sin x$ and $\cos x$ are continuous at $x = 0$.

8. Prove that $\sin x$ is continuous at $x = b$ for every real number b. Suggestion: Write $x = u + b$ so that x tends to b as u tends to zero. Then we get

$$\lim_{x \to b} \sin x = \lim_{u \to 0} \sin(u + b) = \lim_{u \to 0} (\sin u \cos b + \cos u \sin b).$$

CHAPTER 3

INTEGRATION

3.0. We have now developed enough of the theory of limits to continue the study of integral calculus, begun in § 1.6. Our program is to define the integral and to evaluate some specific examples. The definition is not logically completed in this chapter; in order to avoid too much theory too soon, we postpone the question of the existence of the integral in general to Chapter 5 and Appendix A. Our present purpose is to discuss the idea of an integral; existence must wait!

In § 3.6 we shall use the trigonometric identity

$$2 \sin\alpha \sin\beta = \cos(\alpha-\beta) - \cos(\alpha+\beta),$$

which can be obtained by subtracting the well-known identities

$$\cos(\alpha-\beta) = \cos\alpha \cos\beta + \sin\alpha \sin\beta,$$

and

$$\cos(\alpha+\beta) = \cos\alpha \cos\beta - \sin\alpha \sin\beta.$$

3.1 The Limit of a Sum. Having studied the limit process in some measure of detail, we return to our examination of the concept of an integral. In Chapter 1 we computed the area A between the curve $y = x^2$ and the x-axis, from $x = 0$ to $x = 1$. This was done by showing geometrically that A lies between the sums of the areas of two sets of rectangles. Thus we had the inequalities in formula (4) of § 1.6,

$$\sum_{j=1}^{n} \frac{(j-1)^2}{n^3} < A < \sum_{j=1}^{n} \frac{j^2}{n^3}.$$

The sum on the left can be written as

$$\sum_{j=1}^{n-1} \frac{j^2}{n^3},$$

and thus the two sums differ by a single term n^2/n^3 or $1/n$. But $\lim 1/n = 0$ as n tends to infinity, so that the above inequalities show that A is caught between two values whose difference is tending to zero. Thus we can obtain A by using the limit of either sum,

$$A = \lim_{n\to\infty} \sum_{j=1}^{n} \frac{(j-1)^2}{n^3} \quad \text{or} \quad A = \lim_{n\to\infty} \sum_{j=1}^{n} \frac{j^2}{n^3}.$$

The fact that the difference between these two sums tends to zero tells us that if one limit exists so does the other, by Corollary 3 of § 2.4. To the second of the above limits we apply formula (3) of § 1.5 (and also Theorem 12 of § 2.4 and Corollary 10 of § 2.3). Thus we get

$$A = \lim_{n\to\infty} \sum_{j=1}^{n} \frac{j^2}{n^3} = \lim \frac{1}{n^3} \sum_{j=1}^{n} j^2$$

$$= \lim \frac{1}{n^3} \left(\frac{n^3}{3} + \frac{n^2}{2} + \frac{n}{6} \right) = \lim \frac{1}{3} + \lim \frac{1}{2n} + \lim \frac{1}{6n^2}$$

$$= \frac{1}{3} + 0 + 0 = \frac{1}{3}.$$

The notation used in calculus for the limit of the sum just calculated is

$$\int_0^1 x^2 \, dx,$$

"the integral of x^2 from $x = 0$ to $x = 1$". In general the notation for the integral of x^2 from $x = a$ to $x = b$, where $a < b$, is

$$\int_a^b x^2 \, dx,$$

and it represents the following limit of a sum,

$$(1) \qquad \lim_{n\to\infty} \sum_{j=1}^{n} \left\{ a + j\frac{b-a}{n} \right\}^2 \frac{b-a}{n}.$$

We next explain how this formula (1) arises.

Geometrically, this limit can be interpreted as the area bounded above by $y = x^2$, below by the x-axis, and at the sides by the vertical lines $x = a$ and $x = b$ (Figure 3.1). The portion of the x-axis from $x = a$ to $x = b$ is divided into n parts each of length $(b-a)/n$, thus giving us $n+1$ points

$$(x_0, 0), (x_1, 0), (x_2, 0), \ldots, (x_n, 0),$$

where x_0 is just another way of writing a, x_n another way of writing b, and in general

$$(2) \qquad\qquad x_j = a + j\,\frac{b - a}{n}.$$

Vertical lines (called *ordinates*) are constructed from these $n + 1$ points up to the curve $y = x^2$, as illustrated in Figure 3.2 for $(x_{j-1}, 0)$ and

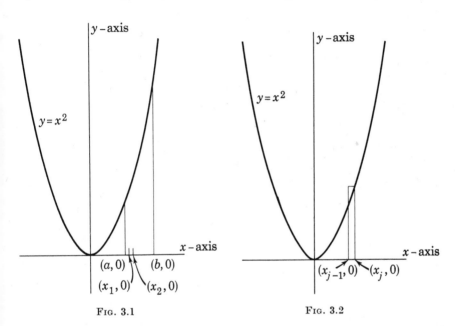

Fɪɢ. 3.1   Fɪɢ. 3.2

$(x_j, 0)$. The rectangle in Figure 3.2 has base $(b - a)/n$ and height $x_j{}^2$, and so has area

$$x_j{}^2 \cdot \frac{b - a}{n} \quad \text{or} \quad \left\{ a + j\,\frac{b - a}{n} \right\}^2 \frac{b - a}{n}$$

by use of (2). Thus the sum in (1) represents the total area of the rectangles illustrated in Figure 3.3. For purposes of illustration we have used $n = 10$, and it is intuitively clear that as n tends to infinity the sum of the areas of the rectangles tends to the area under the curve.

We note that (1) could be written, in view of (2),

$$\int_a^b x^2 \, dx = \lim_{n \to \infty} \sum_{j=1}^{n} x_j{}^2 \cdot \frac{b - a}{n} = \lim_{n \to \infty} \sum_{j=1}^{n} x_j{}^2 (x_j - x_{j-1}).$$

In general, if we replace x^2 by a function $f(x)$ we can write

$$(3) \qquad \int_a^b f(x)\, dx = \lim_{n \to \infty} \sum_{j=1}^n f(x_j)\frac{b-a}{n} = \lim_{n \to \infty} \sum_{j=1}^n (x_j - x_{j-1})f(x_j).$$

The first expression is read "the integral of $f(x)$ from a to b". The geometric interpretation of this is analogous to Figure 3.3 with $y = x^2$ replaced by the curve $y = f(x)$. Thus the integral (3) can be interpreted geometrically as an area, as in Figure 3.4, bounded by $y = f(x)$ above, the x-axis below, the line $x = a$ on the left, and the line $x = b$ on the right.

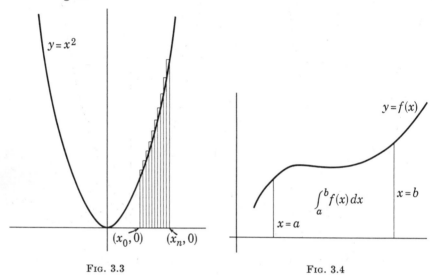

FIG. 3.3   FIG. 3.4

Although an integral is understood most readily as an area, it is not so defined. By defining an integral more formally as a limit of a certain kind of sum, we will have a more general concept than area. The idea of a limit of a sum, or an integral, is adaptable in many places in mathematics. Thus area is merely one interpretation of an integral.

Problems

1. Express the integral $\int_0^1 x\, dx$ as a limit of a sum, and evaluate this limit by use of equation (2) of §1.5.

2. Verify the answer to the preceding question by noting that the integral represents the area of the triangle with vertices $(0, 0)$, $(1, 0)$ and $(1, 1)$.

3. Express the integral $\int_0^2 x\, dx$ as a limit of a sum, and evaluate this limit.

4. Verify the answer to the preceding question by observing that the

integral represents the area of the triangle with vertices $(0, 0)$, $(2, 0)$ and $(2, 2)$.

5. Express the integral $\int_0^1 1 \, dx$, usually written more simply as $\int_0^1 dx$, as a limit of a sum. Evaluate this limit, and then verify the answer by noting that the integral represents the area of the rectangle bounded by $(0, 0)$, $(0, 1)$, $(1, 1)$, and $(1, 0)$.

6. Express the integral $\int_0^1 3x \, dx$ as a limit of a sum, and evaluate the limit. Verify the answer by calculating the area of the appropriate triangle.

7. Express the integral $\int_0^1 3x^2 \, dx$ as a limit of a sum, and evaluate it.

8. Taking formula (3) as a definition, prove that

$$\int_a^b \{f(x) + g(x)\} \, dx = \int_a^b f(x) \, dx + \int_a^b g(x) \, dx,$$

assuming the existence of all limits that occur.

9. Under the same conditions as in the preceding problem, prove that for any constant k

$$\int_a^b k f(x) \, dx = k \int_a^b f(x) \, dx.$$

10. Verify that in general it is *not* true that

$$\int_a^b f(x) g(x) \, dx = \int_a^b f(x) \, dx \cdot \int_a^b g(x) \, dx,$$

by examining the particular case where $f(x) = x$, $g(x) = x$, $a = 0$, $b = 1$.

3.2 The General Definition of an Integral.

In equation (3) the base line on the x-axis from $x = a$ to $x = b$, called the *interval* from $x = a$ to $x = b$, was divided into n *subintervals*, each of length $(b - a)/n$. While this is satisfactory as far as it goes, it is not sufficiently general. It turns out, as we shall see, that the value of the integral is not changed if we divide the interval from $x = a$ to $x = b$ on the x-axis into n subintervals which are not required to be equal in length. Thus the value x_0 is still indentified with a, and x_n with b, but the intermediate points x_1, x_2, ..., x_{n-1} are spaced between a and b without the subintervals being necessarily of equal length. Thus the lengths $x_1 - x_0$, $x_2 - x_1, x_3 - x_2, ..., x_n - x_{n-1}$ may be all different. However, a condition must be imposed, namely, that the largest of these lengths must tend to zero as n tends to infinity.

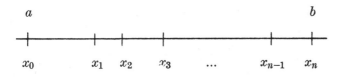

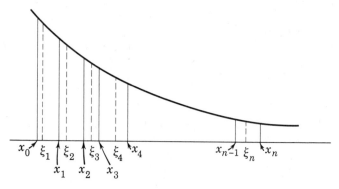

FIG. 3.5

Furthermore, there is no need, as in equation (3), to use $f(x_j)$ in the sum: We can replace it by $f(\xi_j)$, where ξ_j is any value between x_{j-1} and x_j, thus $x_{j-1} \leqq \xi_j \leqq x_j$. So the general definition of an integral is given by

$$(4) \qquad \int_a^b f(x)\,dx = \lim_{n\to\infty} \sum_{j=1}^n (x_j - x_{j-1})f(\xi_j),$$

if this limit exists, where is is understood that the largest one of the numbers $x_1 - x_0$, $x_2 - x_1$, $x_3 - x_2$, ..., $x_n - x_{n-1}$ tends to zero as n tends to infinity. Figure 3.5 illustrates the use of unequal values $x_2 - x_1$, $x_3 - x_2$, etc.

One advantage of this more general definition is that we can evaluate many integrals that are virtually unmanageable by the less general definition (3). This point is illustrated in problems 4, 5, and 6 at the end of this section.

This definition of an integral implies at once that

$$(5) \qquad \int_a^b f(x)\,dx = \int_a^c f(x)\,dx + \int_c^b f(x)\,dx, \quad \text{if} \quad a < c < b.$$

Equation (5) is illustrated in Figure 3.6; the total area is equal to the sum of the areas of the two parts into which it is divided by the line PQ.

From an analytic point of view, equation (5) can be seen from the definition (4) in this way: Suppose that the interval from $x = a$ to $x = b$ on the x-axis is divided

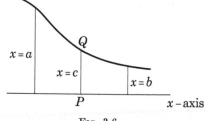

FIG. 3.6

into n parts, with the point $x = c$ always one of the division points. Then the sum in (4) can be separated into two parts around the division point $x = c$, and these separate parts of the sum give the two integrals on the right side of equation (5).

Before discussing further properties of the integral, let us consider whether the definition (4) really defines something. For after all, the integral is defined as a limit, and as we have seen, limits do not necessarily exist. Moreover, the limit in equation (4) is not as simple as those discussed in Chapter 2; the limit is now to be taken over many possible points of division x_1 x_2, ..., x_{n-1}, and many possible intermediate points ξ_1 ξ_2, ..., ξ_n. Thus the definition (4) is not a simple limit of a single sequence. It is the limit of a whole class of sequences, and hence the definition (4) makes sense only if the limit exists and has the same value for all possible choices of the sets of division points x_1, x_2, ..., x_{n-1} and all possible intermediate points ξ_1, ξ_2, ..., ξ_n. Thus we see that there is much more involved in the limit (4) than in the limits discussed in Chapter 2. The limit (4) does not in fact exist for all conceivable functions $f(x)$, but it does exist for the fairly simple types of functions with which we deal, such as x, x^2, x^3, $\sin x$, and $\cos x$.

Proving the existence of the integral is one of the most basic parts of the theory underlying calculus. We postpone this proof in order to develop first some of the needed background, and to permit the reader to gain more familiarity with the notation. In Chapter 5 we prove the existence of the integral in a restricted setting which covers virtually all cases in this book. Then in Appendix A we remove one of the restrictions to get a more general theory covering all the situations that we treat. These proofs will not rely on any intuitive ideas about geometry.

In the present chapter we shall presume that the *integrand* $f(x)$ in the integral $\int_a^b f(x)\, dx$ is an *integrable function*, meaning that it is a function for which the limit (4) exists. Since the limit given in equation (3) is just a special case of (4), we are presuming *a fortiori* that (3) exists.

In all developments of the theory we shall use (4) as the definition of the integral. But in evaluating integrals, it is usually easier to employ the special case (3). The full justification for this procedure will be given in Chapter 5 and Appendix A.

The discussion of equation (4), and the illustration of its meaning in Figure 3.5, have suggested that the number a is always to be taken less than the number b, that is $a < b$. There is no necessity for this restriction in the formulation of an integral. The numbers a and b in $\int_a^b f(x)\, dx$, called the *lower* and *upper limits* of the integral, can satisfy any one of the three possibilities $a > b$, $a < b$, or $a = b$. (Notice that the word "limit" is being used in a different way here; a and b are not limits of the type discussed in Chapter 2.) We now extend the definition of an integral to cover all these cases.

The extended definitions are suggested by either (4) or (5). If for example we want (5) to hold for all possible sets of values a, b, c, then the replacement of c by a suggests the definition

$$\int_a^a f(x)\,dx = 0.$$

This would also be suggested by the interpretation of this integral as an area between $x = a$ and $x = a$. Next, if we replace b by a in (5) we get

$$\int_a^a f(x)\,dx = \int_a^c f(x)\,dx + \int_c^a f(x)\,dx,$$

which, in view of the preceding equation, suggests that the integral from a to c is the negative of the integral from c to a. Hence we assert the following equation as a definition, reverting to the symbols a and b as the limits of integration,

(6) $$\int_a^b f(x)\,dx = -\int_b^a f(x)\,dx.$$

With these definitions it turns out that (5) holds whatever the relation between a, b, and c, provided of course that $f(x)$ is an integrable function. We give no proof of this, but the reader is asked to prove it in a few special cases in the problem set of this section.

The case $c = 0$ of equation (5) is especially useful, namely

$$\int_a^b f(x)\,dx = \int_a^0 f(x)\,dx + \int_0^b f(x)\,dx.$$

Applying (6) to the second of these three integrals we get

(7) $$\int_a^b f(x)\,dx = \int_0^b f(x)\,dx - \int_0^a f(x)\,dx.$$

Finally, we point out that there is no requirement in the definition (4) of an integral that the integrand $f(x)$ be positive. In case $f(x)$ is negative for some values of x, the sum of terms $(x_j - x_{j-1})f(\xi_j)$ is obtained nevertheless, and then the limit is taken as n tends to infinity. This more general meaning of an integral has some marked consequences for the interpretation as an area; we shall discuss this matter in detail in § 3.4.

Problems

1. Taking equation (5) for granted for all numbers a, b, c such that $a \leqq c \leqq b$, and presuming the definition (6), establish the following results:

(a) $\displaystyle\int_4^1 f(x)\,dx = \int_3^1 f(x)\,dx - \int_3^4 f(x)\,dx;$

(b) $\displaystyle\int_2^5 f(x)\,dx = \int_4^5 f(x)\,dx - \int_4^2 f(x)\,dx;$

(c) $\displaystyle\int_1^2 f(x)\,dx + \int_3^1 f(x)\,dx - \int_3^2 f(x)\,dx = 0;$

(d) $\displaystyle\int_1^2 f(x)\,dx + \int_2^3 f(x)\,dx + \int_3^4 f(x)\,dx + \int_4^1 f(x)\,dx = 0.$

2. Combine the sum

$$\int_5^7 f(x)\,dx + \int_7^{10} f(x)\,dx$$

into a single integral.

3. Combine the collection

$$\int_2^4 f(x)\,dx - \int_6^4 f(x)\,dx + \int_6^8 f(x)\,dx$$

into a single integral.

*4. Evaluate the integral

$$\int_0^1 \sqrt{x}\,dx$$

by taking $\xi_j = x_j = j^2/n^2$ in formula (4) of the text. Suggestion: Formulas (2) and (3) of § 1.5 may be helpful. (Note that this problem illustrates the evaluation of an integral by the use of subintervals of unequal length.)

*5. Evaluate the integral

$$\int_1^2 \frac{1}{x^2}\,dx$$

by the following steps.

(a) Prove that

$$\frac{1}{n+j-1} - \frac{1}{n+j} = \frac{1}{(n+j)(n+j-1)}.$$

(b)   By summing this equation for $j = 1, 2, 3, \ldots, n$, prove that

$$\sum_{j=1}^{n} \frac{1}{(n+j)(n+j-1)} = \frac{1}{n} - \frac{1}{2n} = \frac{1}{2n}.$$

(c)   For positive real numbers u and v with $u < v$, prove that

$$u < \sqrt{uv} < v.$$

(d)   Moving towards the use of formula (4) of the text with sub-intervals of equal length, prove that

$$x_j - x_{j-1} = \frac{1}{n}, \quad x_j = \frac{n+j}{n}, \quad \frac{n+j-1}{n} \leq \xi_j \leq \frac{n+j}{n}.$$

(e)   Prove that these inequalities are satisfied if ξ_j is chosen as

$$\xi_j = \sqrt{(n+j)(n+j-1)/n^2}.$$

(f)   Then show that formula (4) gives

$$\int_1^2 \frac{1}{x^2} \, dx = \lim_{n \to \infty} \sum_{j=1}^{n} \frac{1}{n} \cdot \frac{n^2}{(n+j)(n+j-1)},$$

and this can be evaluated by the use of step (b). (Note that this problem and the next illustrate the evaluation of integrals with ξ_j chosen not equal to x_j.)

*6.   Evaluate the integral

$$\int_1^2 \frac{1}{\sqrt{x}} \, dx$$

by the following steps.

(a)   Prove that the inequalities $x_{j-1} \leq \xi_j \leq x_j$ are satisfied if we choose

$$\xi_j = \frac{x_j + x_{j-1} + 2\sqrt{x_j x_{j-1}}}{4}$$

and use step (c) of the preceding problem.

(b)   Prove that this expression for ξ_j can be written as

$$\xi_j = \left\{ \frac{\sqrt{x_j} + \sqrt{x_{j-1}}}{2} \right\}^2.$$

(c)   Taking $f(x) = 1/\sqrt{x}$ with this value of ξ_j, show that formula (4) gives

$$\int_1^2 \frac{1}{\sqrt{x}} \, dx = \lim_{n \to \infty} \sum_{j=1}^{n} (x_j - x_{j-1}) \cdot \frac{2}{\sqrt{x_j} + \sqrt{x_{j-1}}}.$$

(d) Verify that

$$\sum_{j=1}^{n} (x_j - x_{j-1}) \frac{2}{\sqrt{x_j} + \sqrt{x_{j-1}}} = 2\sum \{\sqrt{x_j} - \sqrt{x_{j-1}}\} = 2\{\sqrt{2} - \sqrt{1}\},$$

and so finish the evaluation of the integral.

3.3 The Evaluation of Certain Integrals. Although the general definition (4) of an integral as a limit of a sum does not require equal divisions of the base line as in the earlier, less general, form (3) of the definition, nevertheless we shall use (3) for our calculations. For example, to evaluate the integral $\int_a^b x^2\,dx$, we shall use the form (1) because it is the special case of (3) for the particular function $f(x) = x^2$. We begin with the case where $a = 0$ and $b \geqq 0$, thus

$$\int_0^b x^2\,dx = \lim_{n\to\infty} \sum_{j=1}^{n} \left(\frac{jb}{n}\right)^2 \cdot \frac{b}{n} = \lim_{n\to\infty} \sum_{j=1}^{n} \frac{j^2 b^3}{n^3}.$$

Since the sum is over values of j, we can factor out b^3/n^3 and then use formula (3) of § 1.5, thus

$$\int_0^b x^2\,dx = \lim\left[\frac{b^3}{n^3} \sum_{j=1}^{n} j^2\right] = \lim\left[\frac{b^3}{n^3}\left(\frac{n^3}{3} + \frac{n^2}{2} + \frac{n}{6}\right)\right]$$

$$= \lim\left[b^3\left(\frac{1}{3} + \frac{1}{2n} + \frac{1}{6n^2}\right)\right].$$

Next we apply Theorems 11 and 12 of § 2.4 and Corollary 10 of § 2.3 to get

$$(8) \quad \int_0^b x^2\,dx = b^3\left\{\lim\left(\frac{1}{3} + \frac{1}{2n} + \frac{1}{6n^2}\right)\right\}$$

$$= b^3\left\{\lim\frac{1}{3} + \lim\frac{1}{2n} + \lim\frac{1}{6n^2}\right\} = b^3\left\{\frac{1}{3} + 0 + 0\right\} = \frac{b^3}{3}.$$

This analysis is adequate in case $b \geqq 0$. In case $b < 0$ we use (6) and (3) to write

$$\int_0^b x^2\,dx = -\int_b^0 x^2\,dx = -\lim \sum_{k=1}^{n} \left(b - \frac{kb}{n}\right)^2 \left(-\frac{b}{n}\right).$$

Now we observe that

$$\sum_{k=1}^{n} \left(b - \frac{kb}{n}\right)^2 = \sum_{k=1}^{n} \left\{\frac{b(n-k)}{n}\right\}^2 = -b^2 + \sum_{j=1}^{n} \left\{\frac{jb}{n}\right\}^2,$$

$$\int_0^b x^2\,dx = \lim(-b^2)\left(\frac{b}{n}\right) + \lim \sum_{j=1}^{n} \left\{\frac{jb}{n}\right\}^2 \cdot \frac{b}{n}.$$

The first of these limits is zero, and the second is $b^3/3$ by the analysis in the case $b \geq 0$. Hence formula (8) holds for any real number b.

THEOREM 1. *For any numbers a and b,*

$$\int_a^b x^2\, dx = \frac{b^3}{3} - \frac{a^3}{3}.$$

PROOF. We use (8) and (7) to get

$$\int_a^b x^2\, dx = \int_0^b x^2\, dx - \int_0^a x^2\, dx = \frac{b^3}{3} - \frac{a^3}{3}.$$

THEOREM 2. *For any numbers a and b,*

$$\int_a^b dx = b - a \quad and \quad \int_a^b x\, dx = \frac{b^2}{2} - \frac{a^2}{2}.$$

PROOF. As in equations (8) preceding Theorem 1, we begin with $a = 0$, $b \geq 0$ and prove that

$$(9) \qquad \int_0^b dx = b \quad and \quad \int_0^b x\, dx = \frac{b^2}{2}.$$

These results can be obtained by the use of the definition (3), with $f(x)$ replaced by 1 and x respectively. First, if $f(x) = 1$ we have

$$\int_0^b dx = \lim_{n \to \infty} \sum_{j=1}^n \frac{b}{n} \cdot 1 = \lim\left\{\frac{b}{n} + \frac{b}{n} + \ldots + \frac{b}{n}\right\} = \lim\{b\} = b.$$

In the second case with $f(x) = x$, we use (2) to observe that

$$x_j = \frac{bj}{n}, \quad f(x_j) = x_j = \frac{bj}{n},$$

and so

$$\int_0^b x\, dx = \lim_{n \to \infty} \sum_{j=1}^n \frac{b}{n} \cdot \frac{bj}{n} = \lim \sum \frac{b^2 j}{n^2} = \lim \frac{b^2}{n^2} \sum j.$$

Using formula (2) of § 1.5 we get

$$\int_0^b x\, dx = \lim \frac{b^2}{n^2} \cdot \frac{n(n+1)}{2} = \lim \frac{b^2}{2}\left(1 + \frac{1}{n}\right) = \frac{b^2}{2}\lim\left(1 + \frac{1}{n}\right) = \frac{b^2}{2}.$$

Hence we have established (9) in case $b \geq 0$. For $b < 0$ some such analysis as that following formula (8) is again required; we omit the details because the calculations are so similar. To finish the proof of the theorem we use (7) again. Thus we get

$$\int_a^b dx = \int_0^b dx - \int_0^a dx = b - a,$$

and

$$\int_a^b x\,dx = \int_0^b x\,dx - \int_0^a x\,dx = \frac{b^2}{2} - \frac{a^2}{2}.$$

Equations (9) can be interpreted quite simply in terms of areas. The integral $\int_0^b dx$ denotes the area of the rectangle in Figure 3.7, and $\int_0^b x\,dx$ the area of the triangle in Figure 3.8.

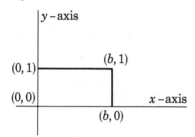

FIG. 3.7 $f(x) = 1.$ FIG. 3.8 $f(x) = x.$

Problems

1. Evaluate the integrals

$$\int_1^2 x^2\,dx, \quad \int_1^5 x^2\,dx, \quad \int_{-1}^5 x^2\,dx,$$

by use of Theorem 1.

2. Evaluate the following integrals:

(a) $\displaystyle\int_2^4 x\,dx$ (c) $\displaystyle\int_0^9 dx$

(b) $\displaystyle\int_2^5 x\,dx$ (d) $\displaystyle\int_0^9 x^2\,dx$

3. Evaluate the integral $\int_0^1 x^3\,dx$ by expressing it as a limit of a sum, and also by using the answer to Problem 12 of § 1.5.

4. Evaluate the integrals

$$\int_0^b x^3\,dx \quad \text{and} \quad \int_a^b x^3\,dx.$$

5. Evaluate the integral $\int_0^a x^4\,dx$, given the information

$$\sum_{j=1}^n j^4 = (6n^5 + 15n^4 + 10n^3 - n)/30.$$

6. Evaluate the integrals

$$\int_0^b x^4\,dx \quad \text{and} \quad \int_a^b x^4\,dx.$$

7. Use Theorem 1 to write algebraic expressions for the values of

$$\int_a^b x^2\,dx, \quad \int_a^c x^2\,dx, \quad \int_c^b x^2\,dx.$$

Check that these algebraic expressions satisfy equation (5) of § 3.2 with $f(x)$ replaced by x^2.

3.4 The Interpretation of an Integral as an Area. The interpretation of $\int_a^b f(x)\,dx$ as an area, as illustrated in Figure 3.4, needs some revision in case $a > b$, and in case $f(x)$ is negative over part or all of the interval from $x = a$ to $x = b$. Now in case $a = b$ the integral has value zero, and this harmonizes with the idea of an area bounded by identical lines $x = a$ and $x = b$. Furthermore, in view of formula (6) there is no need to consider any cases other than $a < b$, because (6) enables us to write any integral with the lower and upper limits satisfying this inequality.

So we presume that every integral $\int_a^b f(x)\,dx$ under discussion has $a < b$. It follows that $x_j - x_{j-1}$ in (4) is positive. Now consider the case where $f(x) \leq 0$ for all values of x from a to b. Then the integral given by (4) will also be less than or equal to zero. The value of the integral will be the *negative* of the area; the term "area" as used here is always a positive or zero quantity, never negative.

As an example consider

$$\int_{-2}^{-1} x\,dx = \frac{(-1)^2}{2} - \frac{(-2)^2}{2} = -\frac{3}{2}.$$

Thus the area between the line $y = x$ and the x-axis, bounded on the left and right by the vertical lines $x = -2$ and $x = -1$, is $3/2$.

Let us turn to the situation where $f(x)$ is positive for part of the range of integration, and negative for another part. In such a case the value of the integral will be positive or negative depending on the dominance of the positive or negative portions of $f(x)$. For example, by Theorem 2 we have

$$\int_{-1}^{3} x\,dx = \frac{9}{2} - \frac{1}{2} = 4, \quad \int_{-3}^{1} x\,dx = \frac{1}{2} - \frac{9}{2} = -4,$$

and these integrals correspond to Figures 3.9 and 3.10. The individual

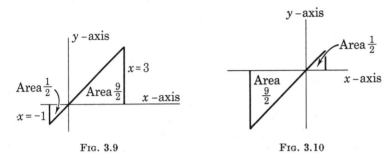

Fig. 3.9   Fig. 3.10

areas in Figure 3.9 correspond to the integrals

$$\int_{-1}^{0} x\,dx = -\frac{1}{2}, \quad \int_{0}^{3} x\,dx = \frac{9}{2},$$

and in Figure 3.10

$$\int_{-3}^{0} x\,dx = -\frac{9}{2}, \quad \int_{0}^{1} x\,dx = \frac{1}{2}.$$

Moreover we see that $\int_{-3}^{3} x\,dx = 0$ without evaluating the integral because we can write

$$\int_{-3}^{3} x\,dx = \int_{-3}^{0} x\,dx + \int_{0}^{3} x\,dx$$

and the last two integrals cancel because they are equal but opposite in sign. This would be the case not only for the function $y = x$ but for any odd power of x such as $y = x^3$, $y = x^7$, or $y = x^7$, as for example

$$\int_{-3}^{3} x^3\,dx = 0, \quad \int_{-3}^{3} x^7\,dx = 0.$$

The point is simply that the graphs of these functions are similar to the graph of $y = x$ in the sense that the graph is below the x-axis to the left of the origin, and above to the right, with a symmetric relationship from the third to the first quadrant. The graph of $y = x^3$ is given in Figure 4.5 on page 103. (In Chapter 5 we will establish the theory needed to evaluate $\int_a^b x^n\,dx$. For the moment we will get a few fragmentary results by area interpretation.)

On the other hand if we take an even power of x like $y = x^2$ or $y = x^4$, the symmetric relationship on the left and right of the origin is even more direct; the y-axis forms a "mirror" for the two parts of the graph. This is illustrated for $y = x^2$ in Figure 1.6 on page 7. Thus we see that

$$\int_0^5 x^2\,dx = \int_{-5}^0 x^2\,dx, \quad \int_{-5}^5 x^2\,dx = \int_{-5}^0 x^2\,dx + \int_0^5 x^2\,dx = 2\int_0^5 x^2\,dx.$$

These results can be checked by calculation of the integrals.

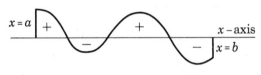

FIG. 3.11

Thus the integral of $f(x)$ from a to b, with $a < b$, has a positive or negative value depending on whether the areas above the x-axis dominate, or those below.

Problems

1. Given that

$$\int_0^1 x^4\,dx = \frac{1}{5}, \quad \int_1^2 x^5\,dx = \frac{21}{2}, \quad \int_1^2 x^4\,dx = \frac{31}{5},$$

evaluate the following by area interpretations:

(a) $\displaystyle\int_{-1}^0 x^4\,dx$ (e) $\displaystyle\int_{-2}^{-1} x^5\,dx$

(b) $\displaystyle\int_{-1}^1 x^4\,dx$ (f) $\displaystyle\int_{-2}^2 x^4\,dx$

(c) $\displaystyle\int_0^2 x^4\,dx$ (g) $\displaystyle\int_{-2}^2 x^5\,dx$

(d) $\displaystyle\int_{-1}^{-2} x^4\,dx$ (h) $\displaystyle\int_0^{2\pi} \sin x\,dx$

2. For any odd positive integer n, evaluate

$$\int_{-1}^{1} x^n \, dx.$$

3. Show that

$$\int_{0}^{\pi} \sin x \, dx = 2 \int_{0}^{\pi/2} \sin x \, dx.$$

4. Show that

$$\int_{0}^{\pi/2} \sin x \, dx = \int_{0}^{\pi/2} \cos x \, dx.$$

5. Evaluate the integrals

$$\int_{0}^{b} \sqrt{x} \, dx \quad \text{and} \quad \int_{a}^{b} \sqrt{x} \, dx$$

where a and b are non-negative real numbers. Suggestion: Apply formula (4) of § 3.2 to the first integral, taking $x_j = \xi_j = bj^2/n^2$.

6. Using the answer to the preceding question, find the area enclosed by the curve $y = \sqrt{x}$ and the lines $y = 0$ and $x = 3$.

7. Find the area enclosed between $y = x^2$ and $y = 4$.

8. Find the area enclosed between $y = x^2$ and $y = x$.

3.5 Further Evaluation of Integrals. In § 3.3 we evaluated some integrals by means of the equation (3). This is the hard way to do the calculation, as we shall see in Chapter 5 where the fundamental theorem of calculus is obtained. But even within the present restricted theory we can derive some techniques for the evaluation of an integral.

THEOREM 3. *If $f(x)$ and $g(x)$ are integrable functions from $x = a$ to $x = b$ then*

$$\int_{a}^{b} [f(x) \pm g(x)] \, dx = \int_{a}^{b} f(x) \, dx \pm \int_{a}^{b} g(x) \, dx,$$

where the plus signs go together, and the minus signs go together. Furthermore, for any constant c

$$\int_{a}^{b} cf(x) \, dx = c \int_{a}^{b} f(x) \, dx.$$

PROOF. By (4) we have

$$\int_{a}^{b} [f(x) \pm g(x)] \, dx = \lim_{n \to \infty} \sum_{j=1}^{n} (x_j - x_{j-1})[f(\xi_j) \pm g(\xi_j)].$$

But by simple algebra we can write

$$(x_j - x_{j-1})[f(\xi_j) \pm g(\xi_j)] = (x_j - x_{j-1})f(\xi_j) \pm (x_j - x_{j-1})g(\xi_j),$$

$$\sum_{j=1}^{n} (x_j - x_{j-1})[f(\xi_j) \pm g(\xi_j)] = \sum_{j=1}^{n} (x_j - x_{j-1})f(\xi_j) \pm \sum_{j=1}^{n} (x_j - x_{j-1})g(\xi_j).$$

Taking limits as n tends to infinity, and using Theorem 12 of Chapter 2, we get the first part of the theorem.

Turning to the second part of the theorem, we see that

$$\int_a^b cf(x)\,dx = \lim_{n \to \infty} \sum_{j=1}^{n} (x_j - x_{j-1})cf(\xi_j).$$

But c, a constant factor, can be factored out of the sum to give

$$\int_a^b cf(x)\,dx = \lim_{n \to \infty} c \sum_{j=1}^{n} (x_j - x_{j-1})f(\xi_j).$$

Next we apply Theorem 11 of Chapter 2, and the proof of the theorem is complete.

EXAMPLE. Evaluate

$$\int_2^5 (x^2 + x)\,dx.$$

Applying Theorems 3, 1, and 2, we get

$$\int_2^5 (x^2 + x)\,dx = \int_2^5 x^2\,dx + \int_2^5 x\,dx = \frac{5^3}{3} - \frac{2^3}{3} + \frac{5^2}{2} - \frac{2^2}{2} = \frac{99}{2}.$$

Problems

1. Evaluate the integrals

(a) $\displaystyle\int_1^3 (x^2 - 1)\,dx$

(c) $\displaystyle\int_0^1 (5x^2 + 6x)\,dx$

(b) $\displaystyle\int_2^3 (x^2 - 2x)\,dx$

(d) $\displaystyle\int_{-3}^3 (x^2 - x - 1)\,dx$

2. Using the data given in Problem 1 of § 3.4, evaluate the integrals

(a) $\displaystyle\int_0^1 5x^4\,dx$

(c) $\displaystyle\int_1^2 (x^5 - x^4)\,dx$

(b) $\displaystyle\int_0^2 10x^4\,dx$

(d) $\displaystyle\int_1^2 (2x^5 - 5x^4)\,dx$

3. Find all values of b to satisfy

$$\int_2^b (x+1)\, dx = 20.$$

4. Find all values of c so that

$$\int_7^{10} (2x+c)\, dx = 90.$$

5. If $f(x)$ and $g(x)$ are integrable functions from $x = a$ to $x = b$, prove that

$$\int_a^b \{c_1 f(x) + c_2 g(x)\}\, dx = c_1 \int_a^b f(x)\, dx + c_2 \int_a^b g(x)\, dx.$$

3.6 The Integral of sin x.

We will need the identity

$$(10) \quad \sin x + \sin 2x + \sin 3x + \ldots + \sin nx = \frac{\cos(x/2) - \cos\{[(2n+1)x]/2\}}{2\sin(x/2)},$$

which holds for all values of x for which $\sin(x/2)$ is not zero. Equation (10) can be established in the following way. Taking the well-known trigonometric identity.

$$2\sin\alpha\sin\beta = \cos(\alpha-\beta) - \cos(\alpha+\beta),$$

we apply it n times to get

$$2\sin x \sin\frac{x}{2} = \cos\frac{x}{2} - \cos\frac{3x}{2}$$

$$2\sin 2x \sin\frac{x}{2} = \cos\frac{3x}{2} - \cos\frac{5x}{2}$$

$$2\sin 3x \sin\frac{x}{2} = \cos\frac{5x}{2} - \cos\frac{7x}{2}$$

$$\cdots$$

$$2\sin(n-1)x \sin\frac{x}{2} = \cos\frac{(2n-3)x}{2} - \cos\frac{(2n-1)x}{2}$$

$$2\sin nx \sin\frac{x}{2} = \cos\frac{(2n-1)x}{2} - \cos\frac{(2n+1)x}{2}.$$

Adding these equations we have

$$2\sin\frac{x}{2}[\sin x + \sin 2x + \sin 3x + \ldots + \sin nx] = \cos\frac{x}{2} - \cos\frac{(2n+1)x}{2}.$$

Dividing by $2 \sin(x/2)$, we get (10).

Now we use this result to evaluate

$$\int_0^b \sin x\, dx$$

for any positive b. From definition (3) it follows that this integral has the meaning

$$\lim_{n\to\infty} \sum_{j=1}^{n} \left[\sin\frac{jb}{n} \right] \cdot \frac{b}{n} = \lim \frac{b}{n} \cdot \sum \sin\frac{jb}{n}.$$

The last sum can be evaluated by means of (10) with x replaced by b/n, thus

$$\sum_{j=1}^{n} \sin\frac{jb}{n} = \frac{\cos(b/2n) - \cos\{[(2n+1)b]/2n\}}{2 \sin(b/2n)}.$$

Hence we have

$$\int_0^b \sin x\, dx = \lim_{n\to\infty} \frac{b}{n} \cdot \frac{\cos(b/2n) - \cos\{[(2n+1)b]/2n\}}{2 \sin(b/2n)}$$

$$= \lim \left[\cos\frac{b}{2n} - \cos\frac{(2n+1)b}{2n} \right] \cdot \frac{(b/2n)}{\sin(b/2n)}.$$

Now as n tends to ∞, $b/2n$ tends to 0, and so by equation (10) of § 2.7,

$$\lim_{n\to\infty} \frac{(b/2n)}{\sin(b/2n)} = \lim_{\theta\to 0} \frac{\theta}{\sin\theta} = 1.$$

Furthermore as n tends to ∞, we observe that

$$\lim \cos\frac{b}{2n} = \cos 0 = 1,$$

and

$$\lim \cos\frac{(2n+1)b}{2n} = \lim \cos\left[b\left(1 + \frac{1}{2n}\right) \right] = \cos b.$$

Combining these results, we obtain

(11) $$\int_0^b \sin x\, dx = 1 - \cos b.$$

Although this has been proved only for $b > 0$, it can be extended at once to $b = 0$ and $b < 0$ by simple area considerations.

THEOREM 4. *For any numbers a and b,*

$$\int_a^b \sin x \, dx = \cos a - \cos b.$$

PROOF. The result follows at once from (11) and (7).

The integral in Theorem 4 is the last that we will evaluate from the definition. As we go from the simpler functions, like x, x^2, and $\sin x$, in the integrand to the more complex functions, the evaluation of the limit of the sum by the methods of this chapter becomes more and more difficult, and certainly impractical even if not impossible. For example, although we have just integrated $\sin x$, there is no comparable technique for evaluating*

$$\int_a^b \tan x \, dx,$$

because there is no simple formula for

$$\tan x + \tan 2x + \tan 3x + \ldots + \tan nx$$

such as we had for the sine series in formula (10). In Chapter 5 we shall discuss the fundamental theorem of calculus, and it will enable us to bypass such lengthy evaluations as in the present section by getting at the integration process through the back door, differentiation.

Problems

1. Evaluate the integrals

(a) $\displaystyle\int_0^{\pi/6} \sin x \, dx$ (c) $\displaystyle\int_0^{\pi} \sin x \, dx$

(b) $\displaystyle\int_0^{\pi/2} \sin x \, dx$ (d) $\displaystyle\int_{\pi/6}^{\pi/3} 4 \sin x \, dx$

2. Evaluate

$$\int_0^{\pi/2} \cos x \, dx.$$

Suggestion: See Problem 4 of § 3.4.

3. Evaluate the integrals

(a) $\displaystyle\int_0^{\pi/2} (\sin x + \cos x) \, dx$ (c) $\displaystyle\int_{\pi/4}^{\pi/2} \cos x \, dx$

(b) $\displaystyle\int_0^{\pi/4} \sin x \, dx$ (d) $\displaystyle\int_0^{\pi} (x + \sin x) \, dx$

* The evaluation of this integral is Problem 11 in § 7.3.

4. Find the area of the region between the curve $y = \sin x$ and the straight line from $(0, 0)$ to $(5\pi/6, 1/2)$.

5. Consider the region between the curve $y = \sin x$ and the x-axis from $x = 0$ to $x = \pi/2$. For what constant c does the line $x = c$ split this region into parts of equal area?

6. Prove that

$$\int_a^b \cos x \, dx = \sin b - \sin a.$$

Suggestion: The graph of $y = \cos x$, if moved a distance $\pi/2$ to the right with the axes remaining fixed, is translated into the graph of $y = \sin x$. Hence the integral of this question, denoting the area between the curve $y = \cos x$ and the x-axis from $x = a$ to $x = b$, can be formulated as another integral denoting the area between the curve $y = \sin x$ and the x-axis from $x = a + \pi/2$ to $x = b + \pi/2$.

3.7 The Volume of a Sphere. The integral is defined as a limit of a sum, not as an area. The reason for this is that the concept of a limit of a sum has much wider ramifications than area. Although many of the applications of the integral concept are beyond the scope of this book, we shall treat some results other than areas bounded by curves. In this section we derive the formula for the volume of a sphere, assuming that we are given the formula for the volume of a circular cylinder.

Let us take, as in Figure 3.12, a semicircle of radius r and center at

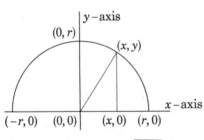

FIG. 3.12 $y = \sqrt{r^2 - x^2}$.

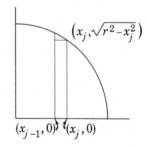

FIG. 3.13

$(0, 0)$. If (x, y) is any point on the semicircle, then the right triangle formed by the points $(0, 0)$, $(x, 0)$ and (x, y) has sides of length $|x|$, y, and r. By Pythagoras' theorem it follows that $x^2 + y^2 = r^2$, and this is the equation of the circle. Solving this equation for y we get

$$y = \sqrt{r^2 - x^2} \quad \text{and} \quad y = -\sqrt{r^2 - x^2}.$$

Our interest is in the first of these formulas, because it is the equation of the semicircle shown in Figure 3.12. The second equation pertains to the other half of the circle below the x-axis, not shown in Figure 3.12. If the semicircle $y = \sqrt{r^2 - x^2}$ is revolved about the x-axis, it sweeps out a sphere in 3-dimensional space, and this is the sphere whose volume we will compute. It actuality we will confine attention to the quarter circle from the point $(0, r)$ on the y-axis down to the point $(r, 0)$ on the x-axis, and so when this is revolved about the x-axis we get exactly half a sphere.

Let us divide the portion of the x-axis from $(0, 0)$ to $(r, 0)$ into n equal parts, giving us the points $(0, 0)$, $(x_1, 0)$, $(x_2, 0)$, ..., $(x_n, 0)$ where x_n is the same as r. Thus $x_j = (jr)/n$ for $j = 1, 2, ..., n$. On each subdivision we construct a rectangle as in Figure 3.13.

Since $x_j - x_{j-1} = r/n$, the rectangle has base r/n and height $\sqrt{r^2 - x_j^2}$. The volume of a half-sphere will be obtained by conceiving of the whole graph of Figure 3.13 as being revolved in space about the x-axis, so that the quarter circle generates a half-sphere of radius r. The rectangle in Figure 3.13 generates a cylinder of radius $\sqrt{r^2 - x_j^2}$ and height r/n, as illustrated in Figure 3.14. The volume of this cylinder is

$$\pi(\sqrt{r^2 - x_j^2})^2 r/n = \pi(r^2 - x_j^2)r/n,$$

and if we sum these volumes from x_1 to x_n and then take the limit as n tends to infinity, we will obtain the volume of the half sphere. Thus if V denotes the volume of a sphere of radius r, we have

FIG. 3.14   (12) $$V = 2 \lim_{n \to \infty} \sum_{j=1}^{n} \pi(r^2 - x_j^2)r/n.$$

This limit can be compared with the right side of equation (3), where $f(x_j)$ is interpreted as $\pi(r^2 - x_j^2)$, and $(b-a)/n$ has the value r/n if we take $b = r$ and $a = 0$. Hence we can write

$$V = 2 \int_0^r \pi(r^2 - x^2)\, dx,$$

and this can be evaluated by use of Theorems 3, 1, and 2, to give

$$V = 2 \int_0^r \pi r^2\, dx - 2 \int_0^r \pi x^2\, dx$$

$$= 2\pi r^2 \int_0^r dx - 2\pi \int_0^r x^2\, dx$$

$$= 2\pi r^2(r) - 2\pi \frac{r^3}{3} = \frac{4}{3}\pi r^3.$$

Note that at the stage where we had equation (12) there is some question of the existence of the limit. We could have established this existence by using the results about limits in § 2.8. However what we did was to use Theorem 3 of § 3.5 instead.

What has been done for the special case of the sphere suggests at once the following generalization. If the graph of $y = f(x)$ from $x = a$ to $x = b$ is revolved about the x-axis, the volume of the solid thus formed is

$$\int_a^b \pi\{f(x)\}^2\, dx.$$

This conclusion can be obtained from the analysis above simply by replacing $\sqrt{r^2 - x^2}$ by $f(x)$ and changing the limits of integration from $0, r$ to a, b.

Problems

1. If in the above analysis we had worked with the entire portion of the x-axis from $(-r, 0)$ to $(r, 0)$ instead of just half of this, we would have arrived at the equation

$$V = \int_{-r}^r \pi(r^2 - x^2)\, dx.$$

Verify that this integral leads to the same answer, $V = (4/3)\pi r^3$.

2. Find the volume of the solid figure obtained by revolving the parabola $y = x^2$ from $x = 0$ to $x = 1$ about the x-axis. (Use the data given in problem 1 of § 3.4.)

3. Find the volume of the solid figure (ellipsoid of revolution) obtained by revolving the ellipse $x^2/4 + y^2/9 = 1$ about the x-axis.

4. Find the volume of the ellipsoid of revolution obtained by revolving the ellipse $x^2/a^2 + y^2/b^2 = 1$ about the x-axis.

5. Let r and h be constants. By revolving the straight line $y = r$ from $x = 0$ to $x = h$ about the x-axis, find the volume of the cylinder of radius r and height h.

6. Consider the two parts into which a sphere of radius r is divided by a plane which passes at a distance k from the center of the sphere. Assume of course that $0 < k < r$. Find the volume of the smaller of these two parts.

7. Find the volume of the cone obtained by revolving the line $y = x$ from $x = 0$ to $x = 2$ about the x-axis.

8. By revolving the triangle formed by $(0, 0)$, $(h, 0)$ and (h, r) around the x-axis, derive the formula for the volume of a right circular cone of radius r and height h. Suggestion: The equation of the straight line through $(0, 0)$ and (h, r) is $y = (r/h)x$.

3.8 Summary of Formulas.*

$$\int_a^b dx = b - a \qquad\qquad \int_a^b x\,dx = \frac{b^2}{2} - \frac{a^2}{2}$$

$$\int_a^b x^2\,dx = \frac{b^3}{3} - \frac{a^3}{3} \qquad\qquad \int_a^b \sin x\,dx = \cos a - \cos b$$

$$\int_a^b f(x)\,dx = -\int_b^a f(x)\,dx \qquad\qquad \int_a^b cf(x)\,dx = c\int_a^b f(x)\,dx$$

$$\int_a^b [f(x) \pm g(x)]\,dx = \int_a^b f(x)\,dx \pm \int_a^b g(x)\,dx \ \text{(matching signs)}.$$

* In this and other summaries at the ends of subsequent chapters, the results are given in brief and often incomplete form. For details of possible limitations on the use of the formulas, the reader should consult the fuller statement given in the chapter.

CHAPTER 4

DIFFERENTIATION

4.0. Two problems of differential calculus, or differentiation, were introduced in §§ 1.2 and 1.3. In this chapter we treat this topic in greater detail, starting with the definition of a derivative, going on to techniques of differentiation, and concluding with applications to problems of maxima and minima.

Let us review a few identities from trigonometry that we shall use. The identity $\sin^2 x + \cos^2 x = 1$, which is Pythagoras' theorem written in trigonometric form, is sufficiently well-known to need no explanation. If this is divided throughout by $\cos^2 x$ and then revised slightly, there results another basic identity, $\sec^2 x = 1 + \tan^2 x$. In § 4.4 we use the identity

$$\sin A - \sin B = 2 \sin \frac{A - B}{2} \cos \frac{A + B}{2}.$$

In case the reader is not familiar with this identity, we note that it can be obtained from the well-known identities

$$\sin(\alpha + \beta) = \sin \alpha \cos \beta + \sin \beta \cos \alpha,$$

and

$$\sin(\alpha - \beta) = \sin \alpha \cos \beta - \sin \beta \cos \alpha.$$

For, subtracting these we get

$$\sin(\alpha + \beta) - \sin(\alpha - \beta) = 2 \sin \beta \cos \alpha.$$

If now we write A for $\alpha + \beta$ and B for $\alpha - \beta$, thus

$$\alpha + \beta = A, \ \alpha - \beta = B, \quad \text{so} \quad \alpha = \frac{A + B}{2} \quad \text{and} \quad \beta = \frac{A - B}{2},$$

then we get the identity we wanted. The identity

$$\cos A - \cos B = -\sin \frac{A - B}{2} \sin \frac{A + B}{2},$$

which is also used in § 4.4, can be obtained in a similar way from

$$\cos(\alpha + \beta) = \cos\alpha\,\cos\beta - \sin\alpha\,\sin\beta,$$

and

$$\cos(\alpha - \beta) = \cos\alpha\,\cos\beta + \sin\alpha\,\sin\beta.$$

4.1 The Derivative. In § 1.3 we solved the problem of finding the slope of the curve $y = x^2$ at the point $(3, 9)$. We now run through the

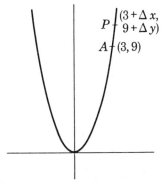

FIG. 4.1   Graph of $y = x^2$.

same solution using notation that is more common to calculus. As in Figure 4.1, consider a fixed point A with coordinates $(3,9)$ on the parabola $y = x^2$, and a nearby point P with coordinates $(3 + \Delta x,\ 9 + \Delta y)$. Thus Δx is the change in the x coordinate, and Δy the change in the y coordinate, measured from the point A to the point P.

The symbol Δ is not a multiplier or a factor when written as part of the notation Δx or Δy. Rather the symbol Δ denotes a difference, so that Δx is the difference in the x coordinates from the point A to the point P, and similarly Δy is the difference in the y coordinates.

The point P, being on the curve, has coordinates which satisfy the equation $y = x^2$; thus

$$9 + \Delta y = (3 + \Delta x)^2 = 9 + 6\Delta x + (\Delta x)^2,$$

$$\Delta y = 6\Delta x + (\Delta x)^2.$$

The slope of the line AP is, by equation (1) of § 1.1,

$$\frac{9 + \Delta y - 9}{3 + \Delta x - 3} = \frac{\Delta y}{\Delta x},$$

and from the preceding equations we have

$$\frac{\Delta y}{\Delta x} = 6 + \Delta x.$$

The tangent line at the point A is the limiting position of the line AP as the point P moves toward A, and so the slope of the tangent line is obtained by letting Δx approach zero; thus

$$\lim_{\Delta x \to 0} \frac{\Delta y}{\Delta x} = \lim_{\Delta x \to 0} (6 + \Delta x) = 6.$$

It should be noted that Δx is not necessarily a positive quantity. The limit above is 6, whether Δx tends to zero through positive values or through negative values. In Figure 4.1, the point P would be "down" the curve from A in case Δx were negative.

Let us generalize from the point $(3, 9)$ to any point A with coordinates (x, y) on the curve $y = x^2$. In this general case the point P would have coordinates $(x + \Delta x, y + \Delta y)$. The points A and P satisfy the equation of the parabola, so we have

$$y = x^2 \quad \text{and} \quad y + \Delta y = (x + \Delta x)^2 = x^2 + 2x\Delta x + (\Delta x)^2.$$

Subtracting these two equations and dividing by Δx, we get

$$\Delta y = 2x\Delta x + (\Delta x)^2,$$

$$\frac{\Delta y}{\Delta x} = 2x + \Delta x,$$

$$\lim_{\Delta x \to 0} \frac{\Delta y}{\Delta x} = \lim_{\Delta x \to 0}(2x + \Delta x) = 2x.$$

It should be emphasized that Δx designates the change in the x coordinate from the point A to the point P, and so Δx is a variable in its own right, independent of x. Thus Δx does not mean some quantity Δ multiplied by some quantity x, but a single quantity.

We have established that the slope of the curve $y = x^2$ at any point on the curve has value $2x$, and the usual notation for this in calculus is

$$\frac{dy}{dx} = 2x$$

Thus dy/dx, called the derivative of y with respect to x, is defined in general by the equation

$$(1) \qquad \frac{dy}{dx} = \lim_{\Delta x \to 0} \frac{\Delta y}{\Delta x}.$$

The process of obtaining $dy/dx = 2x$ from $y = x^2$ is called differentiation, and this is the central process in that part of our subject known as differential calculus. In contrast, the subject matter of Chapter 3 is known as integral calculus.

Example. Differentiate $y = x^3$.

Solution. Using analogous steps to the ones above, we write

$$y = x^3 \text{ for the point } (x, y),$$

$$y + \Delta y = (x + \Delta x)^3 \text{ for the point } (x + \Delta x, y + \Delta y),$$

$$y + \Delta y = x^3 + 3x^2\Delta x + 3x(\Delta x)^2 + (\Delta x)^3,$$

$$\Delta y = 3x^2\Delta x + 3x(\Delta x)^2 + (\Delta x)^3,$$

$$\frac{\Delta y}{\Delta x} = 3x^2 + 3x\Delta x + (\Delta x)^2,$$

$$\frac{dy}{dx} = \lim_{\Delta x \to 0} \frac{\Delta y}{\Delta x} = \lim[3x^2 + 3x\Delta x + (\Delta x)^2] = 3x^2.$$

Thus the slope of the curve $y = x^3$ at any point has value $3x^2$.

Problems

1. Differentiate the following

    (a) $y = x^2 + x$ (c) $y = 2x^3$

    (b) $y = 2x^2$ (d) $y = x^3 - x$

2. Find the slope of each of the curves in Question 1 at the point where $x = 2$.

3. Find the derivative of $y = x^4$.

4. Find the equation of the tangent line to the curve $y = x^2$ at the point $(4, 16)$.

5. Find the equation of the tangent line to the curve $y = x^3$ at the point $(-3, -27)$.

6. Find the point on the curve $y = x^2$ where the slope of the tangent line is 10.

7. At what point or points on the curve $y = x^2$ is the slope equal (a) to the x coordinate? (b) to the y coordinate?

8. At what point or points on the curve $y = x^3$ is the slope equal (a) to the x coordinate? (b) to the y coordinate?

9. Prove that no two tangent lines to the curve $y = x^2$ are parallel.

10. Is there a tangent line to the curve $y = x^3$ which is parallel to the tangent line at the point $(4, 64)$?

11. If A and B are two distinct points on the curve $y = x^3$, under what circumstances is the slope of the curve at A equal to the slope of the curve at B?

12. Prove that the x-axis is a tangent line to the curve $y = x^3$ at the point $(0, 0)$. (This is an example of a tangent line crossing the curve at the point of tangency. Such a point is called a point of inflection.)

4.2 The Definition of the Derivative.

It is desirable to have a definition of *derivative* in a different form than equation (1), a form completely independent of geometric concepts. This we can arrive at by treating a general equation $y = f(x)$ by the process used on $y = x^2$ and $y = x^3$ in § 4.1. We write the equations pertaining to $y = f(x)$ in parallel to those of $y = x^2$, for clarity:

$$y = x^2 \qquad\qquad\qquad y = f(x)$$
$$y + \Delta y = (x + \Delta x)^2 \qquad\qquad y + \Delta y = f(x + \Delta x)$$
$$\Delta y = (x + \Delta x)^2 - x^2 \qquad\qquad \Delta y = f(x + \Delta x) - f(x)$$
$$\frac{\Delta y}{\Delta x} = \frac{(x + \Delta x)^2 - x^2}{\Delta x} \qquad\qquad \frac{\Delta y}{\Delta x} = \frac{f(x + \Delta x) - f(x)}{\Delta x}$$
$$\frac{dy}{dx} = \lim_{\Delta x \to 0} \frac{(x + \Delta x)^2 - x^2}{\Delta x} \qquad \frac{dy}{dx} = \lim_{\Delta x \to 0} \frac{f(x + \Delta x) - f(x)}{\Delta x}.$$

Of these two final equations, the one on the left yields a final simplification

$$\frac{dy}{dx} = 2x,$$

but the one on the right cannot be simplified without specific knowledge about the function $f(x)$. One of the central problems of this chapter is to evaluate dy/dx for various functions $f(x)$. The above equations enable us to reformulate the definition (1).

DEFINITION. *The derivative of a function $f(x)$ is*

$$(2) \qquad\qquad \lim_{\Delta x \to 0} \frac{f(x + \Delta x) - f(x)}{\Delta x},$$

provided this limit exists.

This limit may exist for some values of x and not for others. So we can say that the derivative at $x = c$ is

$$(3) \qquad\qquad \lim_{\Delta x \to 0} \frac{f(c + \Delta x) - f(c)}{\Delta x},$$

provided the limit exists. If the limit (3) exists, we say that the function $f(x)$ is *differentiable* at $x = c$. If the limit (2) exists for every real value of x, we say that the function $f(x)$ is differentiable everywhere. If (2) exists for all x satisfying $a \leq x \leq b$, we say that $f(x)$ is differentiable for this set of values.

In order that a function may be differentiable at $x = c$, the limit (3) must exist. Now as Δx tends to zero, the numerator $f(c + \Delta x) - f(c)$ in (3) must also tend to zero if $f(x)$ is differentiable at $x = c$. Thus the existence of the derivative at $x = c$ implies that

$$\lim_{\Delta x \to 0} f(c + \Delta x) = f(c),$$

and by the definition of a continuous function in § 2.9, this says that $f(x)$ is continuous at $x = c$. Passing from a single point $x = c$ to all the points of an interval we see that we have proved the following result.

THEOREM 1. *If a function $f(x)$ is differentiable at all points of an interval, then $f(x)$ is continuous in that interval.*

We did not specify, because there is no need, whether the interval is of the type $a \leq x \leq b$ (a so-called closed interval), or $a < x < b$ (an open interval), or $a \leq x < b$ or $a < x \leq b$ (half-open).

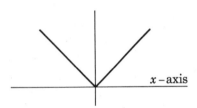

x–axis

FIG. 4.2   Graph of $f(x) = |x|$.

The converse of Theorem 1 is false: a function need not be differentiable at a point just because it is continuous. For example the function $f(x) = |x|$, with graph as in Figure 4.2, is not differentiable at $x = 0$ even though it is a continuous function for every real value of x.

To see why the function $f(x) = |x|$ is not differentiable at $x = 0$, we can look at the geometry of the situation. What is the slope at $(0, 0)$? Is there a well-defined tangent line at $(0, 0)$? In § 1.1 there is a description of the tangent line at a point P of a curve as the limiting position of a segment PQ as Q is moved along the curve toward P. In the present case the point P is $(0, 0)$ and the point Q is along the curve from P. But if Q is along the arm of $f(x) = |x|$ to the left of $(0, 0)$, then the tangent line would be $y = -x$, whereas if Q is to the right of $(0, 0)$, then the tangent line would be $y = x$. Thus there is no unique tangent line and no slope.

Another way of establishing that $f(x) = |x|$ is not differentiable at $x = 0$ is to examine the definition of the derivative in formula (3), with c replaced by zero, thus

$$\lim_{\Delta x \to 0} \frac{f(\Delta x) - f(0)}{\Delta x} = \lim_{\Delta x \to 0} \frac{|\Delta x| - 0}{\Delta x} = \lim_{x \to 0} \frac{|\Delta x|}{\Delta x}.$$

This limit does not exist because if Δx is positive then $|\Delta x|/\Delta x = 1$, whereas if Δx is negative then $|\Delta x|/\Delta x = -1$.

The notation dy/dx has advantages and disadvantages. The principal disadvantage is that it looks like a fraction, which it is not. It is the limit of a fraction, which is quite a different thing. It is the limit of the ratio

$$\frac{\Delta y}{\Delta x} \quad \text{or} \quad \frac{f(x+\Delta x)-f(x)}{\Delta x}$$

as Δx tends to zero. Notice that Δx never actually becomes zero. It is the essential nature of the limit process, as we analyzed it throughout Chapter 2, that a limit has to do with the trend of values of a function up to but not including the critical point.

The advantages of the notation dy/dx for a derivative are its flexibility and convenience. We shall draw attention later to specific instances of what is meant by this.

A REMARK ABOUT NOTATION: Although we have used dy/dx to indicate the derivative of any function $y = f(x)$, other notation for the same thing is often used, for example,

$$y', \quad f'(x), \quad \frac{d}{dx}(y), \quad \frac{d}{dx}f(x), \quad D_x y, \quad D_x f.$$

Thus, the statement "if $y = x^2$ then $dy/dx = 2x$" can be written in the abbreviated form $(d/dx)x^2 = 2x$. There is no reason for restricting this to the variable x; for example

$$\frac{d}{du}(u^2) = 2u, \quad \frac{d}{dt}(t^2) = 2t, \quad \frac{d}{dv}(v^2) = 2v.$$

In the same way the derivative (2) can occur in any variable:

$$f'(x) = \lim_{\Delta x \to 0} \frac{f(x+\Delta x)-f(x)}{\Delta x},$$

$$f'(u) = \lim_{\Delta u \to 0} \frac{f(u+\Delta u)-f(u)}{\Delta u},$$

$$f'(t) = \lim_{\Delta t \to 0} \frac{f(t+\Delta t)-f(t)}{\Delta t}.$$

Since the derivative is the limit of the ratio of Δy to Δx, it is a measure of the rate of change of y with respect to x. For example, consider the function $y = x^2$ with derivative $dx/dy = 2x$. If we think of x as increasing steadily from $x = 0$ to $x = 10$, then y increases at the same time from $y = 0$ to $y = 100$. As x passes through the value 3, y is increasing six times as fast as x, because the derivative is 6. As x passes through the value 7, y is increasing fourteen times as fast as x. Thus the derivative can be thought of as a measure of the rate of change of y compared with the rate of change of x.

Problems

1. Prove that the function $y = x^2$ or $f(x) = x^2$ is continuous for every value of x.
2. Prove that the function $f(x) = x^3$ is continuous for every value of x.
3. Write the derivative of $\sin x$ as a limit.
4. Evaluate

$$\lim_{\Delta x \to 0} \frac{(x+\Delta x)^5 - x^5}{\Delta x}.$$

Suggestion: $(a+b)^5 = a^5 + 5a^4b + 10a^3b^2 + 10a^2b^3 + 5ab^4 + b^5$.
5. Evaluate

$$\lim_{\Delta z \to 0} \frac{(z+\Delta z)^2 - z^2}{\Delta z}.$$

6. If $f(x) = x$, what is $f'(x)$?

4.3 Simple Derivatives. The procedure in § 4.1, by which it was established that the derivative of $y = x^2$ is $dy/dx = 2x$, is too primitive for repeated application to function after function. We now outline some theorems that shorten the work.

To illustrate the next theorem, let us differentiate $y = 5x^2$ by the technique of § 4.1.

$$y = 5x^2,$$

$$y + \Delta y = 5(x + \Delta x)^2 = 5x^2 + 10x\Delta x + 5(\Delta x)^2,$$

$$\Delta y = 10x\Delta x + 5(\Delta x)^2,$$

$$\frac{\Delta y}{\Delta x} = 10x + 5\Delta x,$$

$$\frac{dy}{dx} = \lim_{\Delta x \to 0} (10x + 5\Delta x) = 10x.$$

The constant factor 5 in $y = 5x^2$ stayed in as a multiplier throughout the process.

THEOREM 2. *If $y = cu$ where c is a constant, and u is a differentiable function of x, then*

$$\frac{dy}{dx} = c\frac{du}{dx}.$$

For example, if $u = x^2$ and $c = 5$, then $y = 5x^2$, and from the derivative $du/dx = 2x$ we obtain $dy/dx = 5(2x) = 10x$.

Proof. Let a change Δx in x produce changes Δu and Δy in u and y respectively. Then we have

$$y = cu,$$
$$y + \Delta y = c(u + \Delta u) = cu + c\Delta u,$$
$$\Delta y = c\Delta u,$$
$$\frac{\Delta y}{\Delta x} = c\frac{\Delta u}{\Delta x}, \quad \lim_{\Delta x \to 0} \frac{\Delta y}{\Delta x} = \lim_{\Delta x \to 0}\left[c\frac{\Delta u}{\Delta x}\right],$$
$$\frac{dy}{dx} = c\frac{du}{dx}$$

by Theorem 18 of § 2.8.

Theorem 3. *If $y = c$, then $dy/dx = 0$. If $y = x$, then $dy/dx = 1$.*

Proof. In the first case we have

$$y = c, \quad y = \Delta y = c, \quad \Delta y = 0, \quad \frac{\Delta y}{\Delta x} = 0, \quad \frac{dy}{dx} = 0,$$

and in the second,

$$y = x, \quad y = \Delta y = x + \Delta x, \quad \Delta y = \Delta x, \quad \frac{\Delta y}{\Delta x} = 1, \quad \frac{dy}{dx} = 1.$$

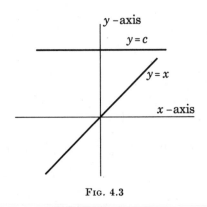

y -axis

$y = c$

$y = x$

x -axis

Fig. 4.3

The geometric interpretation of this theorem is that the line $y = c$ has slope 0, the line $y = x$ has slope 1, as illustrated in Figure 4.3.

In the next three theorems we shall assume that u and v are differentiable functions of x.

Theorem 4. *If $y = u + v$, then $dy/dx = du/dx + dv/dx$. If $y = u - v$, then $dy/dx = du/dx - dv/dx$. Stated alternatively*

$$\frac{d}{dx}(u \pm v) = \frac{d}{dx}(u) \pm \frac{d}{dx}(v) = \frac{du}{dx} \pm \frac{dv}{dx}.$$

PROOF. Let us prove both parts at once by use of the sign $\pm$, denoting plus or minus as the case may be. We can write

$$y = u \pm v,$$
$$y + \Delta y = (u + \Delta u) \pm (v + \Delta v),$$
$$\Delta y = \Delta u \pm \Delta v,$$
$$\frac{\Delta y}{\Delta x} = \frac{\Delta u}{\Delta x} \pm \frac{\Delta v}{\Delta x}.$$

The theorem is obtained from these equations by taking limits as Δx approaches zero, and using Theorem 19 of § 2.8.

EXAMPLE. Differentiate $y = x^2 + x^3$.

Solution. Define u and v as x^2 and x^3 respectively, so that

$$\frac{du}{dx} = 2x, \quad \frac{dv}{dx} = 3x^2, \quad \frac{dy}{dx} = \frac{du}{dx} + \frac{dv}{dx} = 2x + 3x^2.$$

Theorem 4 states in effect that the derivative of a sum equals the sum of the derivatives, and that the derivative of a difference equals the difference of the derivatives. The analog for products does not hold. It is not true in general that the derivative of a product equals the product of the derivatives. For example, the functions x and x^2 have derivatives 1 and $2x$, but their product x^3 does not have derivative $1 \cdot 2x$. However, there is a rule, as the following result shows.

THEOREM 5. *If $y = uv$ then*

$$\frac{dy}{dx} = u\frac{dv}{dx} + v\frac{du}{dx}.$$

Stated alternatively,

$$\frac{d}{dx}(uv) = u\frac{dv}{dx} + v\frac{du}{dx}.$$

PROOF. Again let a change Δx in the independent variable x cause changes Δu, Δv, Δy in the dependent variables u, v, y. Then we have

$$y = uv$$
$$y + \Delta y = (u + \Delta u)(v + \Delta v) = uv + u\Delta v + v\Delta u + (\Delta u)(\Delta v),$$
$$\Delta y = u\Delta v + v\Delta u + (\Delta u)(\Delta v),$$
$$\frac{\Delta y}{\Delta x} = u\frac{\Delta v}{\Delta x} + v\frac{\Delta u}{\Delta x} + \Delta u\frac{\Delta v}{\Delta x}.$$

As Δx tends to zero, so also does Δu. Hence taking limits, we get, by Theorems 19 and 20 of § 2.8,

$$\frac{dy}{dx} = u\frac{dv}{dx} + v\frac{du}{dx} + 0\frac{dv}{dx}$$

$$= u\frac{dv}{dx} + v\frac{du}{dx}.$$

THEOREM 6. *If* $y = u/v$ *then*

$$\frac{dy}{dx} = \frac{v(du/dx) - u(dv/dx)}{v^2}$$

except for values of x *for which* $v = 0$.

PROOF. As in the proof of the preceding theorem we suppose that a change Δx in x produces changes, Δu, Δv, Δy in u, v, y. Then we have

$$y = \frac{u}{v}, \quad y + \Delta y = \frac{u + \Delta u}{v + \Delta v}, \quad \Delta y = \frac{u + \Delta u}{v + \Delta v} - \frac{u}{v},$$

$$\Delta y = \frac{v(u + \Delta u) - u(v + \Delta v)}{v(v + \Delta v)},$$

$$\Delta y = \frac{v\Delta u - u\Delta v}{v(v + \Delta v)}.$$

Dividing by Δx we get

$$\frac{\Delta y}{\Delta x} = \frac{v(\Delta u/\Delta x) - u(\Delta v/\Delta x)}{v(v + \Delta v)}.$$

Finally, we take the limits as Δx tends to zero, and the theorem follows because $v + \Delta v$ tends to v.

THEOREM 7. *If* $y = x^n$, *where* n *is any constant, then*

$$\frac{dy}{dx} = nx^{n-1}.$$

PARTIAL PROOF. Here we establish this for any integer n, and for $n = 1/2$. In § 4.6 we extend the proof to any rational number n, and at the end of § 7.3 we extend it to irrational values of n. Of course, the cases $n = 0, 1, 2, 3$ have been treated earlier in this chapter.

Part 1. Let n be a positive integer. If $n = 4$, $y = x^4$, we can apply Theorem 5 with $u = x$ and $v = x^3$; thus

$$\frac{dy}{dx} = u\frac{dv}{dx} + v\frac{du}{dx} = (x)(3x^2) + (x^3)(1) = 4x^3.$$

Just as this gives the derivative of x^4 from the known derivative of x^3, so we can get the step from x^{n-1} to x^n. If we presume that the derivative of x^{n-1} is $(n-1)x^{n-2}$, then we can apply Theorem 5 with $u = x$ and $v = x^{n-1}$; thus

$$\frac{du}{dx} = 1, \quad \frac{dv}{dx} = (n-1)x^{n-2}, \quad \frac{dy}{dx} = u\frac{dv}{dx} + v\frac{du}{dx},$$

$$\frac{dy}{dx} = (x)(n-1)x^{n-2} + (x^{n-1})(1) = (n-1)x^{n-1} + x^{n-1} = nx^{n-1}.$$

Thus if the theorem holds for any positive integer $n-1$, it holds also for the next integer. Since we have already seen that the theorem holds for $n = 1, 2, 3$ and 4, it follows that the result holds for any positive integer n. (The proof technique that we have used is called "mathematical induction".)

Part 2. Let n be a negative integer, say $n = -m$, where m is a positive integer. Then $y = x^n$ can be written in the form

$$y = \frac{1}{x^m},$$

and we can apply Part 1 above and Theorem 6 to get

$$\frac{dy}{dc} = \frac{x^m(0) - 1(mx^{m-1})}{(x^m)^2},$$

since the derivatives of 1 and x^m are 0 and mx^{m-1}. Hence we have, replacing m by $-n$,

$$\frac{dy}{dx} = \frac{-mx^{m-1}}{x^{2m}} = \frac{-(-n)x^{-n-1}}{x^{-2n}} = nx^{n-1}.$$

Part 3. $n = \frac{1}{2}$. In this case the equation under discussion is $y = x^{1/2}$ or $y = \sqrt{x}$, whose graph is the upper half of a parabola, as illustrated in Figure 4.4. Notice that we are making a distinction between $y = x^{1/2}$ and the full parabola $y^2 = x$. The other half of the parabola, not shown in Figure 4.4, has equation $y = -x^{1/2}$; its graph is symmetric to the graph of $y = \sqrt{x}$ with respect to the x-axis.

For the equation $y = \sqrt{x}$ we have

$$y + \Delta y = \sqrt{x + \Delta x},$$

$$\Delta y = \sqrt{x + \Delta x} - \sqrt{x},$$

$$\frac{\Delta y}{\Delta x} = \frac{\sqrt{x + \Delta x} - \sqrt{x}}{\Delta x}.$$

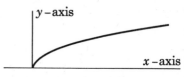

Fig. 4.4   Graph of $y = \sqrt{x}$.

To evaluate the limit as Δx tends to zero, we multiply the fraction on the right, numerator and denominator, by

$$\sqrt{x + \Delta x} + \sqrt{x};$$

thus

$$\frac{\Delta y}{\Delta x} = \frac{\sqrt{x + \Delta x} - \sqrt{x}}{\Delta x} \cdot \frac{\sqrt{x + \Delta x} + \sqrt{x}}{\sqrt{x + \Delta x} + \sqrt{x}},$$

$$\frac{\Delta y}{\Delta x} = \frac{(x + \Delta x) - x}{\Delta x [\sqrt{x + \Delta x} + \sqrt{x}]} = \frac{1}{\sqrt{x + \Delta x} + \sqrt{x}}.$$

As $\Delta x \to 0$, $x + \Delta x \to x$, and hence we have

$$\frac{dy}{dx} = \frac{1}{2\sqrt{x}} = \frac{1}{2}x^{-1/2}.$$

It should be noted that the theorem is to be interpreted for appropriate values of x. For example, in case $n = -1$, we are dealing with the function $y = x^{-1}$ which is not defined at $x = 0$. So of course the derivative has no meaning at $x = 0$. To take another example, let us consider $n = \frac{1}{2}$. The domain of the function $y = x^{1/2}$ is $x \geq 0$, since $x^{1/2}$ is not real-valued for negative values of x. Thus the derivative has no meaning for negative values of x. In fact the derivative has no meaning for $x = 0$, so that the function $y = x^{1/2}$ is differentiable only for $x > 0$.

Problems

1. Differentiate the following:

(a) $y = 7x^2$

(b) $y = 7x^2 + 1$

(c) $y = 7x^2 - 4x + 1$

(d) $y = 5x^6 - x^4$

(e) $y = x^{-3}$

(f) $y = 1/x^4$

(g) $y = 4x$

(h) $y = -1$

2. Extend the proof of Theorem 7 to the case $n = \frac{3}{2}$ by writing $x^{3/2}$ as the product $x \cdot x^{\frac{1}{2}}$, and using Theorem 5.

3. Extend the proof of Theorem 7 to the case $n = \frac{5}{2}$.

4. Extend the proof of Theorem 7 to the case $n = -\frac{1}{2}$.

5. Find the derivatives of the following:

(a) $y = \dfrac{x}{3+x}$

(d) $xy - x^2 - 7 = 0$.

(b) $y = \dfrac{2+x}{x^2}$

(e) $y = \dfrac{\sqrt{x}}{x+3}$

(c) $y = \dfrac{x^2}{x^3 + 3}$

(f) $y = 4\sqrt{x}(x+7) - 3$

6. Given that u, v, and w are differentiable functions of x, find formulas for dy/dx in terms of u, v, w, du/dx, dv/dx, dw/dx in the following cases:

(a) $y = u+v+w$

(d) $y = uvw$

(b) $y = u+v-w$

(e) $y = \dfrac{uv}{w}$

(c) $y = uv-w$

(f) $y = \dfrac{u+v}{w}$

7. Differentiate $y = x^5/x^3$ by using $u = x^5$ and $v = x^3$, and verify that the answer is the same as the derivative of $y = x^2$.

8. Obtain the formula of Theorem 6 by writing $y = u/v$ in the form $u = yv$ and then applying Theorem 5 with u and y interchanged. (Remark: This procedure requires the assumption that y and v be differentiable functions of x. In contrast, the proof given in the text requires, as we noted just prior to Theorem 4, the assumption that u and v are differentiable, and the differentiability of y is a conclusion. In our use of Theorem 6, it will be important to have this property of y as a conclusion, not as an assumption.)

9. For the curve $y = x^2$ prove that $x(dy/dx) = 2y$, and prove that the same relation (differential equation) is satisfied by the curves $y = 2x^2$ and $y = -7x^2$. This suggests that a whole family of curves satisfies this differential equation. Write the general equation for this family of curves by using c as notation for an arbitrary constant.

10. Write the general equation of the family of curves satisfying the differential equation $dy/dx = 6x$.

*11. Let w be a differentiable function of x. If $y = w^2$, prove that $dy/dx = 2w(dw/dx)$. If $y = w^3$, prove that $dy/dx = 3w^2 \cdot dw/dx$. Then use mathematical induction as in part 1 of the proof of Theorem 7 to prove that if $y = w^n$, then $dy/dx = nw^{n-1} \cdot dw/dx$ for every positive integer n.

4.4 Trigonometric Functions.
We shall find the derivatives of $\sin x$, $\cos x$, and $\tan x$, where in all cases x is in radian measure.

THEOREM 8. *If $y = \sin x$, then $dy/dx = \cos x$.*

PROOF. Applying the definition of a derivative, we get

$$y + \Delta y = \sin(x + \Delta x),$$

$$\Delta y = \sin(x + \Delta x) - \sin x,$$

$$\frac{\Delta y}{\Delta x} = \frac{\sin(x + \Delta x) - \sin x}{\Delta x},$$

(4) $$\frac{dy}{dx} = \lim_{\Delta x \to 0} \frac{\sin(x + \Delta x) - \sin x}{\Delta x}.$$

The problem is to evaluate this limit. Recalling the trigonometric identity

$$\sin A - \sin B = 2 \sin \frac{A - B}{2} \cos \frac{A + B}{2},$$

we replace A by $x + \Delta x$ and B by x to get

$$\sin(x + \Delta x) - \sin x = 2 \sin \frac{\Delta x}{2} \cos\left(x + \frac{\Delta x}{2}\right),$$

(5) $$\frac{\sin(x + \Delta x) - \sin x}{\Delta x} = \frac{\sin(\Delta x/2)}{\Delta x/2} \cos\left(x + \frac{\Delta x}{2}\right).$$

In equation (10) of § 2.7 we saw that

$$\lim_{\theta \to 0} \frac{\sin \theta}{\theta} = 1,$$

and so it follows by replacing θ by $\Delta x/2$, that

(6) $$\lim_{\Delta x \to 0} \frac{\sin(\Delta x/2)}{\Delta x/2} = 1.$$

Combining (4), (5), and (6) and applying Theorem 20 of § 2.8, we find that

$$\frac{dy}{dx} = \lim_{\Delta x \to 0} \cos\left(x + \frac{\Delta x}{2}\right) = \cos x.$$

THEOREM 9. *If $y = \cos x$, then $dy/dx = -\sin x$.*

PROOF. The steps are very similar to those in the preceding proof. In the present theorem we need the identity

$$\cos A - \cos B = -2 \sin \frac{A - B}{2} \sin \frac{A + B}{2}.$$

Thus we can write

$$y = \cos x, \quad y + \Delta y = \cos(x + \Delta x),$$

$$\Delta y = \cos(x + \Delta x) - \cos x = -2 \sin \frac{\Delta x}{2} \sin\left(x + \frac{\Delta x}{2}\right),$$

$$\frac{\Delta y}{\Delta x} = -\frac{\sin(\Delta x/2)}{\Delta x/2} \sin\left(x + \frac{\Delta x}{2}\right),$$

$$\frac{dy}{dx} = \lim_{\Delta x \to 0} \frac{\Delta y}{\Delta x} = -\lim \frac{\sin(\Delta x/2)}{\Delta x/2} \cdot \lim \sin\left(x + \frac{\Delta x}{2}\right)$$

$$= -(1)(\sin x) = -\sin x.$$

THEOREM 10. *If $y = \tan x$, then $dy/dx = \sec^2 x$.*

REMARK: This result is not valid, of course, for those values of x for which $\tan x$ is not defined, namely, $x = \pm\pi/2, \pm 3\pi/2, \pm 5\pi/2, \ldots$.

PROOF. By Theorems 6, 8, and 9 we have

$$y = \frac{\sin x}{\cos x},$$

$$\frac{dy}{dx} = \frac{(\cos x)(\cos x) - (\sin x)(-\sin x)}{\cos^2 x}$$

$$= \frac{\cos^2 x + \sin^2 x}{\cos^2 x} = \frac{1}{\cos^2 x} = \sec^2 x,$$

where we have used the identity $\sin^2 x + \cos^2 x = 1$.

Problems

1. Differentiate the following:

(a) $y = \operatorname{cosec} x$ (f) $y = \sin x \cos x$

(b) $y = \sec x$ (g) $y = \sin^2 x$

(c) $y = \cot x$ (h) $y = \sin^3 x$

(d) $y = -5 \sin x$ (i) $y = \cos^2 x$

(e) $xy = \sin x + x$ (j) $y = \sin^2 x + \cos^2 x$

2. Use derivatives to find the following limits:

(a) $\displaystyle \lim_{\Delta x \to 0} \frac{\tan(x + \Delta x) - \tan x}{\Delta x}$

(b) $\displaystyle\lim_{\Delta u \to 0} \frac{\tan(u + \Delta u) - \tan u}{\Delta u}$

(c) $\displaystyle\lim_{\Delta v \to 0} \frac{\cos(v + \Delta v) - \cos v}{\Delta v}$

(d) $\displaystyle\lim_{\Delta x \to 0} \frac{\cos(x + 2\Delta x) - \cos x}{\Delta x}$

3. Find the derivatives of the following:

(a) $y = x \sin x$

(c) $y = \dfrac{\sin x}{x}$

(b) $y = x^2 - \cos x$

(d) $y = \dfrac{\tan x}{(1 + x)^2}$

4. Find the slope of $y = \sin x$ at the point where $x = \pi/3$.

5. Find the equation of the tangent line to the curve $y = \cos x$ at the point $(\pi/6, \sqrt{3}/2)$.

6. Find the equation of the tangent line to the curve $y = \sin x + \cos x$ at the point $(\pi/4, \sqrt{2})$.

7. Prove that the slopes of $y = \sin x$ and $y = \tan x$ are equal at the point $(0, 0)$.

4.5 The Chain Rule. Consider the problem of differentiating $y = (1 + x^3)^5$. With our results so far in this chapter, we would handle this problem by expanding the fifth power of the binomial $1 + x^3$; thus

$$y = 1 + 5x^3 + 10x^6 + 10x^9 + 5x^{12} + x^{15},$$

and using our previous results, we get

(7) $\dfrac{dy}{dx} = 15x^2 + 60x^5 + 90x^8 + 60x^{11} + 15x^{14}.$

It is easier to introduce an intermediate variable u between y and x as follows: $y = u^5$, $u = 1 + x^3$. Then we have

$$\frac{dy}{du} = 5u^4, \quad \frac{du}{dx} = 3x^2.$$

Thus we have separated the original function into two simpler functions whose derivatives are obtained easily, and the next theorem indicates how to combine these derivatives to get dy/dx.

THEOREM 11. *If y is a differentiable function of u, and u is a differentiable function of x, then*

$$\frac{dy}{dx} = \frac{dy}{du} \cdot \frac{du}{dx}.$$

Before turning to the proof of this, let us see how it applies to the problem under discussion just prior to the theorem, namely $y = u^5$, $u = 1 + x^3$. The theorem gives

$$\frac{dy}{dx} = (5u^4)(3x^2) = 15x^2u^4 = 15x^2(1 + x^3)^4.$$

It is perhaps not immediately apparent that this is the same result as in equation (7), but a little simple algebra will establish the equivalence.

PROOF. Any change Δx in the variable x produces a change Δu in the variable u and a change Δy in the variable y. Now by simple algebra we have

$$(8) \qquad \frac{\Delta y}{\Delta x} = \frac{\Delta y}{\Delta u} \cdot \frac{\Delta u}{\Delta x}.$$

Now the assumption that u is a differentiable function of x assures us that as Δx tends to zero so does Δu. So taking limits in (8) as Δx tends to zero we get the equation of the theorem, by using Theorem 20 of § 2.8.

Unfortunately it is not quite so simple. This proof is valid if Δu is not 0, corresponding to any Δx value under consideration. The proof is valid,* for example, for all the problems given at the end of this section, because in each case we can work with sufficiently small values of Δx that $\Delta u \neq 0$. However, in case $\Delta u = 0$, the equation (8) becomes meaningless. Now the theorem is correct even in case $\Delta u = 0$, as the following argument shows.

First whenever $\Delta u = 0$ we observe that $\Delta y = 0$, because y is a function of u; so a zero change in u corresponds to a zero change in y. Now as Δx tends to zero, the corresponding values of Δu may be zero or may not be zero. Define v as the following function of Δu, and so in turn as a function of Δx:

$$v = 0 \text{ in case } \Delta u = 0;$$

$$v = \frac{\Delta y}{\Delta u} - \frac{dy}{du} \text{ in case } \Delta u \neq 0.$$

---

* Indeed, it is valid in every case in this book where Theorem 11 is applied. However, if we wanted to terminate the proof of Theorem 11 with this simple analysis of equation (8), it would be necessary to add another hypothesis to the theorem along these lines: "and if $\Delta u \neq 0$ for sufficiently small non-zero values of Δx."

As Δx tends to zero, so also v tends to zero. Notice that in either of the cases $\Delta u = 0$ or $\Delta u \neq 0$ we have

$$v\Delta u = \Delta y - \Delta u \frac{dy}{du} \quad \text{or} \quad \Delta y = \Delta u \frac{dy}{du} + v\Delta u.$$

Dividing by Δx we get

$$\frac{\Delta y}{\Delta x} = \frac{\Delta u}{\Delta x} \cdot \frac{dy}{du} + v\frac{\Delta u}{\Delta x}.$$

Now let Δx tend to zero, and since v tends to zero, the theorem is proved.

EXAMPLE. Differentiate $y = \sin 5x$.

Solution. Write $y = \sin u$, $u = 5x$, so that by Theorem 8

$$\frac{dy}{du} = \cos u, \quad \frac{du}{dx} = 5, \quad \frac{dy}{dx} = 5 \cos u = 5 \cos 5x.$$

Notice that it is not proper to leave the answer in the form $5 \cos u$, because the variable u was introduced for convenience in solving the problem, but u is not a variable in the original statement of the problem.

Problems

1. Differentiate

(a) $y = \cos 7x$

(b) $y = \tan 3x$

(c) $y = \sqrt{x+1}$

(d) $y = \sqrt{x^2+1}$

(e) $y = (2+x^3)^6$

(f) $y = \cos 2x$

(g) $y = \cos^2 x$

(h) $y = \sin^7 x$

(i) $y = \sqrt{a^2+x^2}$

(j) $y = \sqrt{b^2+(c-x)^2}$

2. Differentiate

(a) $y = \sqrt{\dfrac{4-x^2}{4+x^2}}$

(b) $y = \sin^6 6x$

(c) $y = \dfrac{\sin 4x}{x^2+1}$

(d) $y = \sin x^2$

3. Find the slope of $y = (1+x)^{20}$ at the point on the curve where $x = 0$.

4. Find the slope of $y = \sin 3x$ at $(0, 0)$.

5. Find the derivative of $y = \sqrt{25 - x^2}$. From this find the slope of the tangent line to the circle $x^2 + y^2 = 25$ at the point (3, 4). Remark: This slope can be calculated without the use of calculus, as in problem 14 in § 1.8.

6. Differentiate $y = 2\cos^2 x - 1$, and prove that the answer is the same as in Question 1(f) above.

7. Prove Theorem 9 from Theorem 8 by the use of Theorem 11 and the trigonometric identity

$$\cos x = \sin\left(\frac{\pi}{2} - x\right).$$

Suggestion: Write $y = \sin u$, $u = (\pi/2) - x$.

*8. Find the value of

$$\lim_{\Delta x \to 0} \frac{\sin(2x + 2\Delta x) - \sin 2x}{\Delta x}.$$

*9. Evaluate

$$\lim_{\Delta x \to 0} \frac{\sqrt{x + \Delta x + 3} - \sqrt{x + 3}}{\Delta x}$$

10. Differentiate $y = \sin 2x$ and $y = 2\sin x \cos x$, and show that the derivatives are the same (as they should be since $\sin 2x = 2\sin x \cos x$ is a basic identity of trigonometry).

11. Verify that equation (7) gives the same result for the derivative as the expression $15x^2(1 + x^3)^4$ obtained from Theorem 11.

12. Given the identity $\sin 3x = 3\sin x - 4\sin^3 x$, differentiate both sides to get an identity relating $\cos 3x$, $\sin^2 x$ and $\cos x$.

4.6 Inverse Functions. Consider the function $y = x^3$, with graph as in Figure 4.5. The domain of this function is the set of all real numbers, so that to each real number x there corresponds one real value of y. This function has the property that given two different values of x, the corresponding values of y are also different. On the graph this means that any straight line drawn parallel to the x-axis intersects the curve at not more than one point. Because of this property, we can reverse the correspondence and think of x as a function of y: to each value of y there corresponds a value of x. This is called the *inverse function*, with equation $x = y^{1/3}$. The graph of this equation is the same as the graph of $y = x^3$, as in Figure 4.5.

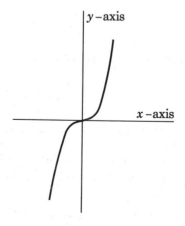

Fig. 4.5 Graph of $y = x^3$ or $x = y^{1/3}$.

Since the graphs of $y = x^3$ and $x = y^{1/3}$ are the same, we can obtain a simple direct relationship between the derivatives of these functions. With respect to $x = y^{1/3}$ we are seeking the derivative with the roles of x and y interchanged; thus

$$\frac{dx}{dy} = \lim_{\Delta y \to 0} \frac{\Delta x}{\Delta y}$$

$$= \lim_{\Delta y \to 0} \frac{(y + \Delta y)^{1/3} - y^{1/3}}{\Delta y}$$

However, Δx and Δy here have exactly the same meaning as for the function $y = x^3$, and as either Δx or Δy tends to zero so does the other. We avoid the point $(0, 0)$ on $y = x^3$, namely the point where the derivative is zero. Hence we can write

(9)
$$\frac{dy\,dx}{dx\,dy} = \lim_{\Delta x \to 0} \frac{\Delta y}{\Delta x} \cdot \lim_{\Delta y \to 0} \frac{\Delta x}{\Delta y}$$

$$= \lim_{\Delta x - 0} \frac{\Delta y}{\Delta x} \cdot \lim_{\Delta x \to 0} \frac{1}{\Delta y/\Delta x}$$

$$= \lim_{\Delta x \to 0} \frac{\Delta y}{\Delta x} \cdot \frac{1}{\Delta y/\Delta x} = 1.$$

Here we are using essentially Theorem 21 of § 2.8.

For $y = x^3$ we know that $dy/dx = 3x^2$, and so from (9) we get

$$\frac{dx}{dy} = \frac{1}{3x^2} = \frac{1}{3}x^{-2} = \frac{1}{3}y^{-2/3} \quad \text{for} \quad x = y^{1/3}.$$

A direct interchange of x and y now gives:

$$\text{If } y = x^{1/3}, \quad \text{then } \frac{dy}{dx} = \frac{1}{3}x^{-2/3},$$

and so we have established another case of Theorem 7 of § 4.3.

To generalize what we have done, we will use the concept of a monotonic function, i.e., roughly speaking one whose graph is rising from left to right, or falling from left to right, as in Figures 4.6 and 4.7.

DEFINITION. *A function $f(x)$ on the interval $a \leq x \leq b$ is said to be monotonic increasing if for any two values of x in the interval, say x_1 and*

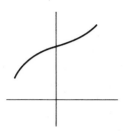

FIG. 4.6 Monotonic increasing function.   FIG. 4.7 Monotonic decreasing function.

x_2 with $x_1 < x_2$, the functional values satisfy the inequality $f(x_1) < f(x_2)$. A function $f(x)$ is said to be monotonic decreasing if under the same circumstances $f(x_1) > f(x_2)$. A function is said to be monotonic if it is either monotonic increasing or monotonic decreasing.

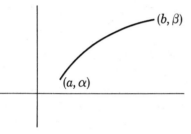

If $y = f(x)$ is monotonic on an interval, it is clear that to different values of x in the interval there correspond different values of $f(x)$. Hence we can reverse the correspondence and think of x as a function of y, say $x = g(y)$. This is the *inverse function*.

FIG. 4.8   Graph of $y = f(x)$ or $x = g(y)$.

THEOREM 12. *Let $y = f(x)$ be monotonic and differentiable, with $f'(x) \neq 0$, on the interval $a < x < b$. Write α and β for $f(a)$ and $f(b)$ respectively, and $x = g(y)$ for the inverse function. Then $x = g(y)$ is a differentiable function on the interval $\alpha < y < \beta$ or $\alpha > y > \beta$ according as $f(x)$ is monotonic increasing or decreasing, and*

$$\frac{dy}{dx} \cdot \frac{dx}{dy} = f'(x) \cdot g'(y) = 1.$$

(The interval $a \leq x \leq b$, a so-called "closed" interval was used in the definition of a monotonic function, whereas we use the "open" interval $a < x < b$ in the present theorem. It could be either way in the definition, but the theorem is more useful with x over an open interval.)

PROOF. The definition of a function and the assumption that $f(x)$ is monotonic assures us that $\Delta x \neq 0$ as long as $\Delta y \neq 0$, and $\Delta y \neq 0$ as long as $\Delta x \neq 0$. Hence we can argue exactly as we did to get equation (9) in the special case of the function $y = x^3$, using in effect the simple algebraic relation

$$\frac{\Delta y}{\Delta x} \cdot \frac{\Delta x}{\Delta y} = 1,$$

and the theorem follows by use of Theorem 21 of § 2.8.

It should be noted that the definition of a monotonic function and Theorem 12 can be adapted to intervals that are not finite. A function $f(x)$ is said to be monotonic increasing on the interval $a < x < \infty$ if for any two values of x in the interval, say x_1 and x_2 with $x_1 < x_2$ the relation $f(x_1) < f(x_2)$ holds. A similar definition applies for intervals $-\infty < x < b$ and $-\infty < x < \infty$. In Theorem 12 the adaptation that must be made is in the meaning of α and β. This will be an easy matter in the cases we deal with. For example, Theorem 12 is applicable to $y = x^3$ or $f(x) = x^3$ on the interval $0 < x < \infty$, with $\alpha = f(a) = f(0) = 0$ and β interpreted as ∞ because as x increases indefinitely so does $f(x)$. The theorem is also applicable to $f(x) = x^3$ on the interval $-\infty < x < 0$ with $\beta = f(b) = f(0) = 0$ and α interpreted as $-\infty$. However, although $f(x) = x^3$ is monotonic increasing on $-\infty < x < \infty$, we cannot apply Theorem 12 to this particular function on this interval because it contains $x = 0$ and we see that $f'(0) = 0$.

Even with finite intervals $a < x < b$ there are situations where not both $f(a)$ and $f(b)$ are defined. For example the function $f(x) = 1/x$ on the interval $0 < x < 1$ is monotonic decreasing, but Theorem 12 needs slight adaptation in this case because $f(0)$ is not defined, although it is clear that $\beta = f(b) = f(1) = 1$. But it is not difficult to see that α can be taken as ∞ because $1/x$ can be made as large as we please by taking positive values of x very close to 0.

Theorems 11 and 12 illustrate one advantage of the notation dy/dx for a derivative. The equations in these theorems would be obvious if the derivative were a fraction with numerator dy and denominator dx. In many cases it is permissible to treat the derivative in just this way, as these theorems establish. Furthermore this notation makes it easy to remember what these theorems assert.

Next we use Theorems 11 and 12 to extend the proof of Theorem 7 of § 4.3 to any rational number n. Theorem 7 has already been established for any integer n. Next let n be the reciprocal of a positive integer, say $n = 1/k$. We want to differentiate the function $y = x^{1/k}$. In order that we may apply Theorem 12, we want to avoid the point $(0, 0)$, so we shall take $0 < x < \infty$ as the domain of the function. For this domain the function is monotonic increasing, and the inverse function is $x = y^k$. The derivative of this is, by Theorem 7,

$$\frac{dx}{dy} = ky^{k-1},$$

and by Theorem 12 we get

$$\frac{dy}{dx} = \frac{1}{ky^{k-1}} = \frac{1}{kx^{1-1/k}} = nx^{n-1}.$$

Now we let n be any rational number, say $n = m/k$, where m and k are integers. Although n may be positive or negative, we may presume that k is positive, absorbing any negative sign into m. We want to differentiate $y = x^{m/k}$, and we write

$$y = u^m, \quad u = x^{1/k},$$

and so

$$\frac{dy}{du} = mu^{m-1}, \quad \frac{du}{dx} = \frac{1}{k} x^{(1/k)-1}.$$

By Theorem 11 we conclude that

$$\frac{dy}{dx} = (mu^{m-1})\left(\frac{1}{k}x^{(1/k)-1}\right)$$

$$= \frac{m}{k}x^{(m-1)/k} \cdot x^{(1-k)/k}$$

$$= nx^{(m-k)/k} = nx^{n-1}.$$

Hence we have proved Theorem 7 for all rational exponents.

Next we turn to the equation $y = \tan x$. To get an inverse function from this it is desirable to restrict severely the domain of values of x.

When we discussed the equation $y = \tan x$ in Theorem 10, the domain was $-\infty < x < \infty$ except for $x = \pm \pi/2, \pm 3\pi/2, \pm 5\pi/2, \ldots$. We now consider what is in effect a different function, namely, $y = \tan x$ with the domain $-\pi/2 < x < \pi/2$, with graph as in Figure 4.9. Inasmuch as this function differs from the one in Theorem 10 only in the narrowing of the domain of values of x, we observe that the conclusion of Theorem 10 is still valid. As illustrated by Figure 4.9, the function under consideration is monotonic increasing, and so it has an inverse function $x = \arctan y$, this being the standard notation from trigonometry. By Theorems 10 and 12 we can write

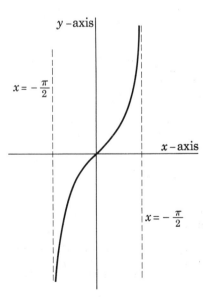

FIG. 4.9 Graph of $y = \tan x$,
$-\pi/2 < x < \pi/2$.

$$\frac{dy}{dx} = \sec^2 x, \frac{dx}{dy} = \frac{1}{\sec^2 x}.$$

From elementary trigonometry we use the well-known identity

$$\sec^2 x = 1 + \tan^2 x,$$

whence

$$\sec^2 x = 1 + y^2 \quad \text{and} \quad \frac{dx}{dy} = \frac{1}{1 + y^2}.$$

Thus we have established the proposition

If $x = \text{arc tan } y$, then $\dfrac{dx}{dy} = \dfrac{1}{1 + y^2}$.

Now if we interchange x and y so as to put this in the more standard form where y is a function of x, we obtain the following result.

THEOREM 13. *The derivative of $y = \text{arc tan } x$ is*

$$\frac{dy}{dx} = \frac{1}{1 + x^2}.$$

It should be kept in mind that the domain of the function $y = \text{arc tan } x$ is $-\infty < x < \infty$ and the range is $-\pi/2 < y < \pi/2$, as in Figure 4.10.

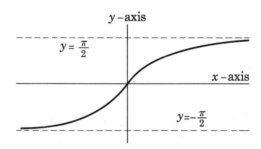

FIG. 4.10   Graph of $y = \text{arc tan } x$.

Problems

1. Prove that the tangent line to the graph of $y = \text{arc tan } x$ at the point $(0, 0)$ has slope 1.

2. Find the x coordinates of the points, if any, on the graph of $y = \text{arc tan } x$ where the curve has slope $\frac{1}{2}$.

3. Find the x coordinates of the points, if any, on the graph of $y = \text{arc tan } x$ where the curve has slope 5.

4. Find the derivatives of the following:

(a) $y = \arctan 2x$ (c) $y = (\arctan x)^2$

(b) $y = 2 + \arctan x$ (d) $y = \arctan\sqrt{x}$

5. Find the derivatives of (a) $y = x^{3/4}$; (b) $y = x^{-4/5}$; (c) $y^3 = x^2$.

6. Find the equation of the tangent line to $y = x^{2/3}$ at the point $(27, 9)$.

7. Find the derivative of $y = \arcsin x$ for the domain $0 \leq x < 1$.

8. Find the derivative of $y = \arccos x$ for the domain $0 \leq x < 1$.

9. The inverse function of $y = f(x) = x^3$ is $x = g(y) = y^{1/3}$. Verify the conclusion of Theorem 12 in this special case.

10. (a) In Theorem 11 let us write $y = g(u)$ and $u = f(x)$. Show that the conclusion of the theorem can now be written in the form

$$\frac{dy}{dx} = g'(u)f'(x).$$

(b) Next eliminate u and show that the conclusion of Theorem 11 can be stated in the form: If $y = g(f(x))$ then

$$\frac{dy}{dx} = g'(f(x))f'(x).$$

(c) Next remove the y and show that the conclusion of Theorem 11 can be stated thus: The derivative of $g(f(x))$ is $g'(f(x))f'(x)$.

11. Prove Theorem 12 by using part (c) of the preceding problem. Suggestion: $x = g(y)$ and $y = f(x)$ imply that $x = g(f(x))$. This equation gives two forms of the same function, and differentiating we get

$$1 = g'(f(x))f'(x) = g'(y)f'(x).$$

4.7 The Mean Value Theorem. We now discuss one of the most important results in calculus.

THEOREM 14. *Suppose that a function $F(x)$ has a derivative $f(x)$ for all x satisfying $a \leq x \leq b$. Then there is a value of x strictly between a and b, say $x = c$ with $a < c < b$, such that*

$$f(c) = \frac{F(b) - F(a)}{b - a} \text{ or } F(b) - F(a) = (b - a)f(c).$$

To give a plausible argument for the truth of this, let us look at the matter geometrically. The quotient $[F(b) - F(a)]/(b - a)$ is the slope of the straight line joining the two points $(a, F(a))$ and $(b, F(b))$ on the graph of $y = F(x)$. Calling these points P and Q respectively, we see that the theorem states that there is at least one point on the graph between P and Q where the tangent line is parallel to PQ. In Figure 4.11 there are two such points.

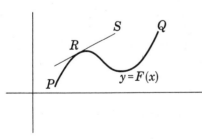

FIG. 4.11

To continue our intuitive argument, let R be any point on the graph $y = F(x)$ between P and Q with the following property The perpendicular distance from R to PQ is a maximum. It is intuitively clear that such a point exists. Next let a straight line RS be drawn through R parallel to PQ. There will be no points of the graph of $y = F(x)$ lying on the far side of RS, that is, the side away from PQ, at least not in the interval $a < x < b$. Thus RS is a tangent line to the curve, and RS is parallel to PQ.

Such an intuitive appeal to the geometry of the situation is not to be regarded as an adequate proof. A rigorous proof must be analytic in nature, that is, it must be based only on the foundations of logic and the real number system, not on geometric intuition. Such a proof is beyond the scope of this book. Our viewpoint is that the mean value theorem is taken as an axiom, and we build the further structure of calculus on it. As a first example of the use of the mean value theorem, we establish a connection between the sign of the derivative and the increase or decrease of a function.

THEOREM 15. *Let $F(x)$ be a differentiable function on $a \leq x \leq b$, such that $F'(x) > 0$ for all x on the open interval $a < x < b$. Then the function $F(x)$ is monotonic increasing on the closed interval $a \leq x \leq b$. In a similar setting, if $F'(x) < 0$ then $F(x)$ is monotonic decreasing.*

PROOF. We prove the first part only, since the second part is analogous. Let x_1 and x_2 be any two numbers in the closed interval such that $x_1 < x_2$, and so $a \leq x_1 < x_2 \leq b$. We apply Theorem 14 to $F(x_2) -F(x_1)$. Thus there is a number c strictly between x_1 and x_2 such that

$$F(x_2) - F(x_1) = (x_2 - x_1)F'(c).$$

Now $F'(c)$ is positive by hypothesis, and so is $x_2 - x_1$. Hence $F(x_2) -F(x_1)$ is positive, and the theorem is established.

The theorem could have been stated more readily if $F'(x) > 0$ had been assumed on the closed interval $a \leq x \leq b$. However, the result so stated would have been weaker, and would not have applied, for example, to the function $F(x) = x^2$ with $a = 0$ and $b = 1$, even though this function *is* monotonic increasing over the interval $0 \leq x \leq 1$. Such an example is not as special as it may seem; it occurs in more general form in the proof of Theorem 17.

Problems

1. Find the c of the mean value theorem (Theorem 14) in each of the following cases:

(i) $F(x) = x(x-1)$, $a = 0$, $b = 2$;

(ii) $F(x) = x(x-1)$, $a = 0$, $b = 1$;

(iii) $F(x) = x(x-1)$, $a = 1$, $b = 2$;

(iv) $F(x) = \sin x + 2x$, $a = 0$, $b = \pi$;

(v) $F(x) = x^3 - x^2$, $a = 0$, $b = 1$.

*2. If α, β, γ are real numbers satisfying $2\alpha + 3\beta + 6\gamma = 0$, prove that $\alpha x^2 + \beta x + \gamma = 0$ has at least one root between 0 and 1. Suggestion: Apply the mean value theorem to $F(x) = 2\alpha x^3 + 3\beta x^2 + 6\gamma x$ with $a = 0$, $b = 1$.

3. Prove that the function $F(x) = x(x-1)$ is monotonic decreasing on $0 \leqq x \leqq \frac{1}{2}$, but monotonic increasing on $\frac{1}{2} \leqq x \leqq 1$.

4. Prove that $x - \sin x$ is monotonic increasing on $0 \leqq x \leqq k$ where k is any positive number. Hence prove that $\sin x < x$ for any positive value of x.

5. Prove that $\tan x > x$ for any x satisfying $0 < x < \pi/2$.

6. For which positive values of x is $y = x - 1/x$ a monotonic increasing function?

7. Prove that arc tan x is a monotonic increasing function of x for all values of x.

8. Prove that $y = x^2 - 4x$ is monotonic increasing for $x \geqq 2$, but monotonic decreasing for $x \leqq 2$.

4.8 Maxima and Minima. The differentiation process can be used in many problems to find the maximum and minimum values of a function. In Figure 4.12 it is intuitively clear that at points A and B,

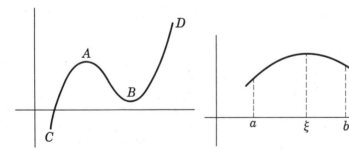

FIG. 4.12 $y = F(x)$.   FIG. 4.13

where the function $F(x)$ has maximum and minimum values, the derivative $F'(x)$ is zero. Note that we are discussing so-called *local* maximum and minimum values, that is to say, maximum and minimum points compared with nearby points on the graph. For example, in Figure 4.12 the values of $F(x)$ in the vicinity of the point C are smaller than at B, and likewise the values of $F(x)$ in the vicinity of the point D are greater than at A. To be specific, we shall say that $F(x)$ is a *maximum* at $x = \xi$ if there is an interval containing ξ, say $a < \xi < b$, such that $F(\xi) > F(x)$ for all values of x satisfying $a \leqq x \leqq b$ except $x = \xi$

itself. The definition of a *minimum* is the same with $F(\xi) > F(x)$ replaced by $F(\xi) < F(x)$. First we establish that $F'(\xi) = 0$ is a necessary condition for a maximum or minimum.

THEOREM 16. *Let $F(x)$ be a function having a derivative for all x satisfying $a \leqq x \leqq b$. Suppose that $F(x)$ is a maximum at a specific value $x = \xi$, where $a < \xi < b$; i.e., suppose that $F(\xi) > F(x)$ for all x in the interval $a \leqq x \leqq b$ except $x = \xi$. Then $F'(\xi) = 0$. Similarly if $F(x)$ is a minimum at $x = \xi$, then $F'(\xi) = 0$.*

PROOF. We restrict our attention to the maximum case, since the minimum case is analogous. The proof is indirect; we show that it is impossible that $F'(\xi) > 0$ or that $F'(\xi) < 0$. First we suppose that $F'(\xi) > 0$. Then by (3) of § 4.2 we see that

$$\lim_{\Delta x \to 0} \frac{F(\xi + \Delta x) - F(\xi)}{\Delta x} > 0.$$

Consider positive values of Δx. Since the limit is positive, the difference $F(\xi + \Delta x) - F(\xi)$ must be positive for Δx sufficiently small. That is, $F(\xi + \Delta x) > F(\xi)$ for small positive values of Δx. But this contradicts our assumption that $F(\xi)$ is a maximum.

On the other hand, suppose that $F'(\xi) < 0$, so that

$$\lim_{\Delta x \to 0} \frac{F(\xi + \Delta x) - F(\xi)}{\Delta x} < 0.$$

Consider now negative values of Δx. Since the limit is negative, the difference $F(\xi + \Delta x) - F(\xi)$ must be positive for Δx sufficiently close to zero. Again this gives us the inequality $F(\xi + \Delta x) > F(\xi)$, which contradicts the assumption that $F(\xi)$ is a maximum.

Since $F'(x) = 0$ at both A and B in Figure 4.12, how can we distinguish a maximum point from a minimum point? To answer this, we recall that the derivative $F'(x)$ can be thought of as the slope of the curve. Thus $F'(x)$ is positive at points on the curve immediately to the left of A, and negative at points immediately to the right. In the vicinity of the point B it is the other way round; $F'(x)$ is negative at points immediately to the left of B, and positive at points immediately to the right. These considerations suggest the following result.

THEOREM 17. *Suppose that a function $F(x)$ has a derivative for all x satisfying $a \leqq x \leqq b$. Suppose furthermore that for a specific value of x between a and b, say $x = \xi$ with $a < \xi < b$, the derivative $F'(x)$ changes from positive to zero to negative as x passes through ξ from left to right:*

$$F'(x) > 0 \quad \text{for} \quad a \leqq x < \xi; \quad F'(x) = 0 \quad \text{for} \quad x = \xi;$$
$$F'(x) < 0 \quad \text{for} \quad \xi < x \leqq b.$$

Then $F(x)$ is a maximum at $x = \xi$ in the sense that $F(\xi) > F(x)$ for every value of x satisfying $a \leq x < \xi$ or $\xi < x \leq b$. Similarly $F(x)$ is a minimum at $x = \xi$ if $F'(x)$ changes from negative to zero to positive as x passes through ξ from left to right.

PROOF. We prove this in the case of a maximum; the case of a minimum is analogous. By Theorem 15 the function $F(x)$ is monotonic increasing on the closed interval $a \leq x \leq \xi$, and monotonic decreasing on the closed interval $\xi \leq x \leq b$. Hence $F(x)$ is a maximum at $x = \xi$.

It can occur that $F'(\xi) = 0$, but that $F'(x)$ does not have different signs to the left and right of $x = \xi$. For example, consider the function $F(x) = x^3$. The derivative is $F'(x) = 3x^2$, so that $F'(0) = 0$. But $F'(x)$ is positive both for $x < 0$ and for $x > 0$. This function assumes neither a maximum nor a minimum value at $x = 0$, as illustrated in Figure 4.5. in § 4.6.

In summary then, we have established in Theorem 16 that in order that a differentiable function $F(x)$ have a maximum or minimum strictly inside an interval $a \leq x \leq b$ it is necessary that $F'(x) = 0$ for some value of x in the interval. However, knowing that $F'(x) = 0$ for a certain value of x is not sufficient to guarantee a maximum or minimum. Additional conditions are set forth in Theorem 17 to assure the presence of a maximum or minimum. Consequently, given a function $F(x)$ we must take two steps to determine its maxima and minima. First we must find all values ξ such that $F'(\xi) = 0$. Second we must apply Theorem 17 to each such value in order to determine whether $F(x)$ is actually a maximum, a minimum, or neither. (In more extended works on calculus, alternatives to Theorem 17 are given, but we limit ourselves to this one result.)

EXAMPLE. For what values of x is $F(x) = x^3 - 12x^2 + 45x - 40$ a maximum or a minimum?

Solution. By Theorem 16 all maxima and minima occur at values of x where $F'(x) = 0$. We note that

$$F'(x) = 3x^2 - 24x + 45;$$
$$F'(x) = 0 \quad \text{if} \quad 3x^2 - 24x + 45 = 0.$$

The solutions of this equation are $x = 3$ and $x = 5$. Furthermore, since $F'(x)$ can be written in the form $3(x-3)(x-5)$, we observe that

$$F'(x) > 0 \text{ for } x < 3, \quad F'(x) < 0 \text{ for } 3 < x < 5, \quad F'(x) > 0 \text{ for } x > 5.$$

Hence $F(x)$ is a maximum at $x = 3$, a minimum at $x = 5$, by Theorem 17.

NOTE. Our discussion of maxima and minima has been restricted to situations where the maximum or minimum occurs at an interior point of the domain of definition of the function. For example in Theorem 16 the maximum or minimum was presumed to be located at $x = \xi$, where $a < \xi < b$. We did not allow $\xi = a$ or $\xi = b$. A consequence of this is that our procedure will not necessarily locate maximum or minimum points at the end of the domain of the function. As an illustration of this, consider the function $y = \sqrt{1-x^2}$. The graph of this is a semicircle, actually the upper half of a circle with radius 1, center at $(0, 0)$. Our procedure, applied to this function, will locate the maximum point at $x = 0$, $y = 1$, but not the minimum points at $x = 1$, $y = 0$ and $x = -1$, $y = 0$. These minimum points are end points of the domain of the function, the domain being $-1 \leqq x \leqq 1$.

Problems

1. Examine the following functions for maximum and minimum values of y:

(a) $y = x^2 - 4x - 4$

(b) $y = 6 + 7x - x^2$

(c) $y = 2x^3 + 3x^2 - 36x + 45$

(d) $y = 2x^3 + 3x^2 - 36x + 42$

(e) $y = x^3 - 6x^2 + 12x + 10$

(f) $y = x^3 - 3x^2 + 3x + 4$

(g) $y = \dfrac{x^2}{x+1}$

(h) $y = x^2 + \dfrac{9}{x}$

(i) $y = 2x^2 + \dfrac{18}{x}$

2. For any fixed numbers k_1, k_2, ..., k_n determine x so that each of the following shall be a minimum:

(a) $(x - k_1)^2$

(b) $(x - k_1)^2 + (x - k_2)^2$

(c) $(x - k_1)^2 + (x - k_2)^2 + (x - k_3)^2$

(d) $(x - k_1)^2 + (x - k_2)^2 + (x - k_3)^2 + \ldots + (x - k_n)^2$.

3. Find two numbers whose sum is 12 and whose product is a maximum.

4. Let c be a positive constant. Find two numbers whose sum is c and whose product is a maximum.

5. Among all rectangles of fixed perimeter p, find the dimensions of the one with largest area.

6. Find the positive number which exceeds its square by the largest amount.

7. Find the positive number which exceeds its cube by the largest amount.

8. Find the positive number such that the sum of the number and its reciprocal is a minimum.

9. Find two numbers with sum 10 such that the result of adding one to the square of the other is a minimum.

10. Find two positive numbers x and y whose sum is 10, (a) such that x^2y is a maximum, (b) such that x^3y is a maximum.

11. Find positive numbers x and y such that $xy = 150$ and such that $2x + 3y$ is a minimum.

12. Find the maximum of each of the following for values of x in the interval $0 < x < \pi/2$:
    (a) $\sin x + \cos x$
    (b) $3 \sin x + 4 \cos x$
    (c) $8 \sin x + - \tan x$

13. Find the point on the curve $y = x^2$ nearest to the point $(2, 1/2)$. Suggestion: Minimize the square of the distance from $(2, 1/2)$ to a point on the curve. Points on the curve can be designated as (x, x^2).

14. Find the point on the curve $y = x^2/2$ nearest to the point $(6, 0)$.

15. What are the dimensions of the rectangular box with no top and with maximum volume, that can be made from a piece of tin 18 inches by 18 inches by cutting equal squares from the corners of this square and then turning up the sides?

16. Among the rectangles with perimeter 100, which has the shortest possible diagonal? Suggestion: Minimize the square of the length of the diagonal instead of the length itself.

4.9 The Problem of Minimum Surface Area of a Cylinder of Fixed Volume.

We return to the problem posed in § 1.2, to find the dimensions of a cylinder of volume 18π with minimum surface area S. The equations were, without repetition of all the details,

$$18\pi = \pi r^2 h, \quad S = 2\pi r^2 + \frac{36\pi}{r} = 2\pi r^2 + 36\pi r^{-1},$$

where r and h denote the radius and height of the cylinder. The derivative is, by Theorem 7,

$$\frac{dS}{dr} = 4\pi r - 36\pi r^{-2},$$

and this equals zero in case

$$4\pi r = 36\pi r^{-2}, \quad r = 9r^{-2}, \quad r^3 = 9, \quad r = \sqrt[3]{9}.$$

For positive values of r less than $\sqrt[3]{9}$ we see that

$$r^3 < 9, \quad 1 < \frac{9}{r^3}, \quad \frac{dS}{dr} = 4\pi r\left(1 - \frac{9}{r^3}\right) < 0.$$

For values of r greater than $\sqrt[3]{9}$ we can write

$$r^3 > 9, \quad 1 > \frac{9}{r^3}, \quad \frac{dS}{dr} = 4\pi r\left(1 - \frac{9}{r^3}\right) > 0.$$

Hence Theorem 17 assures us that S is a minimum when $r = \sqrt[3]{9}$. The other dimension of the cylinder would have the value

$$h = \frac{18}{r^2} = \frac{18}{9^{2/3}} = 2\sqrt[3]{9}.$$

The actual minimum value of S is

$$S = 2\pi r^2 + 2\pi rh = 2\pi(\sqrt[3]{9})^2 + 2\pi(\sqrt[3]{9})(2\sqrt[3]{9}) = 6\pi 9^{2/3}.$$

The use of Theorem 17 could have been dispensed with here. The geometry of the situation assures us that there is a minimum for some positive value of r. Theorem 16 tells us that the derivative is zero at this location. Then our calculation showed that the derivative is zero for a single value of r, and so this must provide the location of the minimum value of S.

Problems

1. Find the dimensions of a cylinder of volume 250 cubic units, if the surface area is to be a minimum.

2. Find the dimensions of a cylinder of surface area 54π square units, if the volume is to be a maximum.

3. Prove that a cylinder of fixed volume has minimum surface area in case $h = 2r$, where h and r denote the height and radius of the cylinder.

4. A rectangular dog run is to be built, using one side of a house and 60 linear feet of fencing. What is the maximum area that can be fenced off?

5. A page of a book is to have area 48 square inches, with 1-inch margins at the top and the bottom of the page, and $\frac{3}{4}$-inch margins at each side. What should be the dimensions of the page so that the space available for printed matter is a maximum?

*6. A right triangle has sides 6, 8, and 10 units long. What are the dimensions of the rectangle of maximum area that can be inscribed, with one side of the rectangle lying along the longest side of the triangle?

*7. In the preceding problem, what would be the answer if two adjacent sides of the rectangle coincide partly with the sides of the triangle of lengths 6 and 8?

*8. What are the dimensions of the cylinder of maximum volume that can be inscribed in a sphere of radius 1?

*9. Given that one base and the two non-parallel sides of a trapezoid are each 6 units long, what should be the length of the fourth side for maximum area?

*10. A cylindrical bin with no top (i.e., one of the circular ends missing) is to be constructed of volume 1000 cubic feet. Find the dimensions for minimum surface area.

*11. A metal cylindrical storage tank of volume 1000 cubic feet is to be constructed. The circular base of the tank is made of metal costing $2 per square foot, whereas the sides and top are of metal costing $1 per square foot. Find the dimensions for minimum cost.

*12. Two points A and B lie in the same plane as, and on the same side of, a certain fixed line. The perpendicular distances from A and B to the line are 16 and 4 units, respectively. The points A and B are 13 units apart, thus AB = 13. A point P is chosen on the line in such a way that AP+PB is a minimum. What is the length PB?

4.10 The Refraction of Light. As light travels from one medium into another, say from water into air, it is refracted in the sense that its path is bent or deflected from travel in a straight line. It is this phenomenon that makes a rod appear bent when it is thrust into water; Figure 4.15 is an illustration of this when the rod is viewed from above

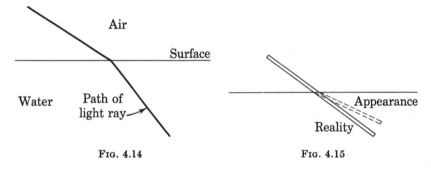

FIG. 4.14   FIG. 4.15

the water but off to one side. The law of the index of refraction (Snell's law) is

$$(10) \qquad \frac{v_1}{v_2} = \frac{\sin \alpha}{\sin \beta}$$

where v_1 is the velocity of light in the upper medium (say air),
v_2 is the velocity of light in the lower medium (say water),
α is the angle of incidence (see Figure 4.16),
β is the angle of refraction (see Figure 4.16).

The ratio of velocities v_1/v_2 is approximately 4/3 in the air-to-water case, so that α is the larger angle, as illustrated.

There is a general law, the minimum principle, that says that light travels from B to A in such a way as to minimize the elapsed time.

We will show that (10) can be deduced from this law. It will also be assumed that light follows a straight line in a homogeneous medium such as air or water. We regard A and B as fixed points, C and D as the points of intersection of the perpendiculars drawn from A and B to the surface separating the media, and P as the point on the surface where the path of light changes direction. Denote the lengths AC, BD, and CD by the constants a, b, and c. Since we do not know at the outset

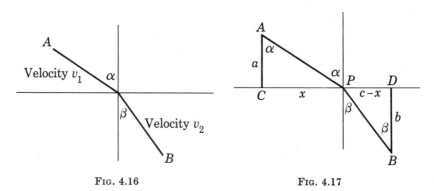

FIG. 4.16   FIG. 4.17

the location of the point P, except that it is on the line CD, we denote the length CP by x, and so PD by $c-x$. Hence we have

$$AP = \sqrt{a^2+x^2}, \quad PB = \sqrt{b^2+(c-x)^2},$$

and so the total time t of passage of the ray of light from A to B via P is

$$t = \frac{\sqrt{a^2+x^2}}{v_1} + \frac{\sqrt{b^2+(c-x)^2}}{v_2},$$

$$t = \frac{1}{v_1}(a^2+x^2)^{1/2} + \frac{1}{v_2}(b^2+c^2-2cx+x^2)^{1/2}.$$

The only variables in this equation are x and t, although we should keep in mind that α and β are also variables in Figure 4.17. We use the above equation to determine the values of x that make t a minimum. Differentiating we get

(11) $$\frac{dt}{dx} = \frac{x}{v_1}(a^2+x^2)^{-1/2} + \frac{-c+x}{v_2}(b^2+c^2-2cx+x^2)^{-1/2}.$$

It is not easy to solve for x when this derivative is equated to zero, so we proceed indirectly. The derivative (11) is zero in case

(12) $\begin{cases} \dfrac{x}{v_1}(a^2+x^2)^{-1/2} = \dfrac{c-x}{v_2}(b^2+c^2-2cx+x^2)^{-1/2} \\[2mm] \dfrac{1}{v_1} \cdot \dfrac{x}{\sqrt{a^2+x^2}} = \dfrac{1}{v_2} \cdot \dfrac{c-x}{\sqrt{b^2+(c-x)^2}}, \\[2mm] \dfrac{1}{v_1}\sin\alpha = \dfrac{1}{v_2}\sin\beta. \end{cases}$

To prove that this result gives a minimum value of t, we must proceed slightly differently than in preceding sections, because we have not computed the actual value of x which $dt/dx = 0$. In view of equations (12) we see that (11) can be written in the form

(13) $$\frac{dt}{dx} = \frac{1}{v_1}\sin\alpha - \frac{1}{v_2}\sin\beta.$$

Let $x = q$ be the value of x for which $dx/dt = 0$. Then from Figure 4.17 we observe that a decrease in x from $x = q$ causes a decrease in α and an increase in β. Since α and β are acute angles, this causes a decrease in $\sin\alpha$ and an increase in $\sin\beta$. From (13) we see that this produces a negative value for dt/dx. Hence for $x < q$ we have $dt/dx < 0$.

On the other hand an increase in x from the value $x = q$ causes an increase in α and a decrease in β, as seen in Figure 4.17. This results in an increase in $\sin\alpha$ and a decrease in $\sin\beta$, and so from (13) we see that dx/dt is positive. We have shown that dx/dt passes from negative to zero to positive as x passes through $x = q$, and hence by Theorem 17 the time t is a minimum when equations (12) are satisfied.

Problem

1. A man is in a rowboat $\frac{1}{2}$ mile from shore at a point P. Presume that the shoreline is approximately straight, and let Q denote the point on the shore closest to the man. The man wants to go to point R which is 3 miles along the shore from Q. Assuming he can row 3 miles per hour and run 6 miles per hour, at what point should he pull the boat up on the shore and run the rest of the way in order to get from P to R in the shortest possible time?

4.11 Summary of Formulas.

$$\frac{d}{dx}(cu) = c\frac{du}{dx}. \qquad\qquad \frac{d}{dx}(u \pm v) = \frac{du}{dx} \pm \frac{dv}{dx}\text{(matching signs)}$$

$$\frac{d}{dx}(uv) = u\frac{dv}{dx} + v\frac{du}{dx} \qquad \frac{d}{dx}\left(\frac{u}{v}\right) = \left[v\frac{du}{dx} - u\frac{dv}{dx}\right]/v^2$$

$$\frac{d}{dx}(x^n) = nx^{n-1} \qquad \frac{d}{dx}(c) = \frac{dc}{dx} = 0$$

$$\frac{d}{dx}(\sin x) = \cos x \qquad \frac{d}{dx}(\cos x) = -\sin x$$

$$\frac{d}{dx}(\tan x) = \sec^2 x \qquad \frac{d}{dx}(\arctan x) = \frac{1}{1+x^2}.$$

The chain rule:

$$\frac{dy}{dx} = \frac{dy}{du} \cdot \frac{du}{dx};$$

see Theorem 11 for details.

$$\frac{dy}{dx} \cdot \frac{dx}{dy} = 1;$$

see Theorem 12 for details.

CHAPTER 5

THE FUNDAMENTAL THEOREM

5.0. The fundamental theorem of calculus shows the close relation between differentiation and integration, enabling us to extend integration far beyond the few cases handled in Chapter 3. It also enables us to prove the existence of the integral for a wide class of functions; the extension to an even wider class of functions is given in Appendix A.

5.1 Derivatives and Integrals. The number of functions $f(x)$ whose integrals were evaluated in Chapter 3 is much smaller than the number of functions whose derivatives were evaluated in Chapter 4. Furthermore, in Chapter 4 we had many more general theorems to enable us to work from the differentiation of one or two functions to a wide class of related functions. This deficiency in our theory of integration will now be remedied in part by a broadening of the class of functions we are able to integrate. To do this, we establish a version of the fundamental theorem of calculus, which (roughly stated) says that integrations and differentiation are reverse processes.

To give an example, in § 3.3 it was established that

$$\int_a^b x^n \, dx = \frac{b^{n+1}}{n+1} - \frac{a^{n+1}}{n+1}$$

in case $n = 0, 1, 2$, and the case $n = 3$ was given as a problem. Inasmuch as the derivative of $x^{n+1}/(n+1)$ is x^n this suggests the general proposition that

(1) $$\int_a^b f(x) \, dx = F(b) - F(a),$$

where $F(x)$ is a function whose derivative is $f(x)$. Another example of this formula (1) is given by Theorem 4 of § 3.6,

$$\int_a^b \sin x \, dx = (-\cos b) - (-\cos a),$$

which is (1) with $f(x)$ replaced by $\sin x$, and $F(x)$ replaced by $-\cos x$.

Equation (1), with appropriate qualifications on the functions $f(x)$ and $F(x)$, is the fundamental theorem of calculus. But first we discuss a preliminary result.

5.2 Upper and Lower Sums. We now return to the definition of an integral as it was given in equation (4) of § 3.2:

$$(2) \qquad \int_a^b f(x)\,dx = \lim_{n\to\infty} \sum_{j=1}^n (x_j - x_{j-1}) f(\xi_j),$$

where $x_0 = a$, $x_n = b$,

$$x_0 \leqq x_1 \leqq x_2 \leqq x_3 \leqq \ldots \leqq x_{n-1} \leqq x_n,$$

ξ_j is any value satisfying $x_{j-1} \leqq \xi_j \leqq x_j$, and the largest of $x_1 - x_0$, $x_2 - x_1$, ..., $x_n - x_{n-1}$ tends to zero as n tends to infinity. This notation and the accompanying conditions will be assumed throughout the rest of the chapter.

In this section we assume that $f(x)$ is monotonic on the interval $a \leqq x \leqq b$ (see § 4.6 for the definition of a monotonic function). Next we define the sums s_n and S_n by the equations

$$(3) \qquad s_n = (x_1 - x_0)f(x_0) + (x_2 - x_1)f(x_1) + (x_3 - x_2)f(x_2) + \ldots$$
$$+ (x_n - x_{n-1})f(x_{n-1}),$$

$$(4) \qquad S_n = (x_1 - x_0)f(x_1) + (x_2 - x_1)f(x_2) + (x_3 - x_2)f(x_3) + \ldots$$
$$+ (x_n - x_{n-1})f(x_n).$$

THEOREM 1. *If $f(x)$ is monotonic increasing, then*

$$s_n \leqq \sum_{j=1}^n (x_j - x_{j-1})f(\xi_j) \leqq S_n$$

If $f(x)$ is monotonic decreasing, the inequalities are reversed.

PROOF. Consider the monotonic increasing case; the other case is analogous. We observe that

$$f(x_{j-1}) \leqq f(\xi_j) \leqq f(x_j),$$

$$(x_j - x_{j-1})f(x_{j-1}) \leqq (x_j - x_{j-1})f(\xi_j) \leqq (x_j - x_{j-1})f(x_j),$$

and the theorem follows when we sum these inequalities from $j = 1$ to $j = n$.

THEOREM 2. *If $f(x)$ is monotonic, then*

$$\lim_{n\to\infty} (S_n - s_n) = 0.$$

PROOF. Again we confine our attention to the monotonic increasing case, since the other case is analogous. We see that

(5) $$S_n - s_n = \sum_{j=1}^{n} (x_j - x_{j-1})[f(x_j) - f(x_{j-1})] \geqq 0.$$

Let t_n denote the maximum of $x_j - x_{j-1}$ for all values $j = 1, 2, 3, ..., n$. Then we can write

(6) $$S_n - s_n \leqq \sum_{j=1}^{n} t_n[f(x_j) - f(x_{j-1})] = t_n \sum_{j=1}^{n} [f(x_j) - f(x_{j-1})].$$

The last sum involves much cancellation because it is

$$[f(x_1) - f(x_0)] + [f(x_2) - f(x_1)] + [f(x_3) - f(x_2)] + \ ...$$

$$+ [f(x_n) - f(x_{n-1})] = -f(x_0) + f(x_n) = f(b) - f(a).$$

Hence (5) and (6) imply that

$$0 \leqq S_n - s_n \leqq t_n[f(b) - f(a)].$$

But $f(b) - f(a)$ is a constant, and $t_n \to 0$ as $n \to \infty$, so we can apply Theorem 9 of § 2.3, with a_n replaced by $t_n[f(b) - f(a)]$ and b_n replaced by $S_n - s_n$. Thus $S_n - s_n \to 0$ as $n \to \infty$, and the proof is complete.

THEOREM 3. *Let $F(x)$ be a differentiable function whose derivative is $f(x)$ on the interval $a \leqq x \leqq b$. Let $f(x)$ be monotonic on this interval. Then with s_n and S_n defined as in (3) and (4),*

(7) $$\lim_{n\to\infty} S_n = \lim_{n\to\infty} s_n = F(b) - F(a).$$

PROOF. Again it suffices to prove this in case $f(x)$ is monotonic increasing. We apply the mean value theorem of § 4.7 to $F(x)$, with a and b replaced by x_0 and x_1. We conclude that there is a value θ_1 between x_0 and x_1 such that

$$F(x_1) - F(x_0) = (x_1 - x_0)f(\theta_1).$$

Similarly there are real numbers θ_2 between x_1 and x_2, θ_3 between x_2 and x_3, ..., θ_n between x_{n-1} and x_n, such that

$$F(x_2) - F(x_1) = (x_2 - x_1)f(\theta_2)$$
$$F(x_3) - F(x_2) = (x_3 - x_2)f(\theta_3)$$
$$\cdot \quad \cdot \quad \cdot$$
$$F(x_n) - F(x_{n-1}) = (x_n - x_{n-1})f(\theta_n).$$

Adding all these equations we get

$$F(x_n) - F(x_0) = (x_1 - x_0)f(\theta_1) + (x_2 - x_1)f(\theta_2) + (x_3 - x_2)f(\theta_3) + \ldots$$
$$+ (x_n - x_{n-1})f(\theta_n).$$

The sum on the right lies between s_n and S_n, by Theorem 1 above. Also $x_n = b$ and $x_0 = a$, so we have

$$s_n \leqq F(b) - F(a) \leqq S_n.$$

To this we apply Theorem 14 of § 2.4, with c replaced by $F(b) - F(a)$, a_n replaced by S_n, and b_n replaced by s_n. In view of Theorem 2, we obtain equations (7).

Problems

1. Compute s_n, S_n and $F(b) - F(a)$ in case $f(x) = 2x$, $F(x) = x^2$, $a = x_0 = 0$, $x_1 = .2$, $x_2 = .4$, $x_3 = .6$, $x_4 = .8$, $b = x_5 = 1$.
2. Compute s_n, S_n, and $F(b) - F(a)$ in case $f(x) = 2x$, $F(x) = x^2$, $a = 0$, $b = 1$, $n = 10$, $x_j = j/10$ for $j = 0, 1, 2, ..., 10$.
3. Compute s_n, S_n, and $F(b) - F(a)$ in case $f(x) = 2x$, $F(x) = x^2$, $a = 0$, $b = 1$, $n = 20$, $x_j = j/20$ for $j = 0, 1, 2, ..., 20$.
4. The same as Question 1, but with $f(x) = 3x^2$, $F(x) = x^3$.
5. The same as Question 2, but with $f(x) = 3x^2$, $F(x) = x^3$.
6. The same as Question 3, but with $f(x) = 3x^2$, $F(x) = x^3$.

5.3 The Fundamental Theorem of Calculus.

Although we do not establish the fundamental theorem for the widest possible class of functions, nevertheless the results we obtain are adequate for all functions within our purview.

THEOREM 4. *Let $F(x)$ be a function with a derivative $f(x)$ on the interval $a \leqq x \leqq b$. If $f(x)$ is monotonic on this interval, then the integral (2) exists and its value is*

$$\int_a^b f(x)\, dx = F(b) - F(a).$$

PROOF. Again we treat only the case where $f(x)$ is monotonic increasing. Write σ_n for the sum in equation (2), that is

$$(8) \qquad \sigma_n = \sum_{j=1}^{n} (x_j - x_{j-1}) f(\xi_j),$$

so that

$$\int_a^b f(x)\, dx = \lim_{n \to \infty} \sigma_n$$

if this limit exists. By Theorem 1 we have

$$s_n \leqq \sigma_n \leqq S_n.$$

To these inequalities we apply Theorem 17 of § 2.4. In view of Theorem 3 above we conclude that

$$\lim_{n \to \infty} \sigma_n = \lim S_n = \lim s_n = F(b) - F(a).$$

Thus $\lim \sigma_n$ exists, and so by (8) the integral exists.

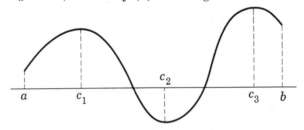

FIG. 5.1 Piecewise monotonic function.

Next we generalize Theorem 4 to functions $f(x)$ that are piecewise monotonic, which means that the graph of $f(x)$ consists of a finite number of pieces each of which is monotonic.

DEFINITION. *A function $f(x)$ is said to be piecewise monotonic on an interval $\alpha \leqq x \leqq b$ if the interval can be separated into a finite number of subintervals*

$$a \leqq x \leqq c_1, \quad c_1 \leqq x \leqq c_2, \ldots, \quad c_{j-1} \leqq x \leqq c_j, \quad c_1 \leqq x \leqq b,$$

such that $f(x)$ is monotonic on each subinterval.

THEOREM 5. *Let $F(x)$ be a function with a derivative $f(x)$ on the interval $a \leqq x \leqq b$. If $f(x)$ is piecewise monotonic on this interval, then the integral (2) exists and is equal to*

$$\int_a^b f(x)\, dx = F(b) - F(a).$$

Proof. First we prove the result in the case of two subintervals, that is, if $f(x)$ is monotonic on two subintervals $a \leq x \leq c$ and $c \leq x \leq b$, then it is integrable on the interval $a \leq x \leq b$, and moreover

$$(9) \qquad \int_a^b f(x)\,dx = \int_a^c f(x)\,dx + \int_c^b f(x)\,dx.$$

(This is formula (5) of § 3.2, but the explanation given at that stage of the development *assumed* that $f(x)$ was an integrable function over *every* interval under discussion.) Since c lies in the interval $a \leq x \leq b$ it must lie in one of the subintervals of formula (2), say $x_k \leq c \leq x_{k+1}$. Now we can write

$$S = \sum_{i=1}^n (x_i - x_{i-1}) f(\xi_i)$$

$$= \sum_{i=1}^k (x_i - x_{i-1}) f(\xi_i) + \sum_{i=k+1}^n (x_i - x_{i-1}) f(\xi_i).$$

Since $(c - x_k)f(c) + (x_{k+1} - c)f(c) - (x_{k+1} - x_k)f(c) = 0$, we can formulate the sum S as $S = A + B + C$ where

$$A = \sum_{i=1}^k (x_i - x_{i-1}) f(\xi_i) + (c - x_k)f(c),$$

$$B = (x_{k+1} - c)f(c) + \sum_{i=k+1}^n (x_i - x_{i-1}) f(\xi_i),$$

$$C = -(x_{k+1} - x_k)f(c).$$

As n tends to infinity, A and B tend to the two integrals on the right side of equation (9), by use of Theorem 4 since $f(x)$ is monotonic over $a \leq x \leq c$ and $c \leq x \leq b$. Also C tends to zero because $x_{k+1} - x_k$ does. This establishes (9).

Having established (9) for two subintervals, we apply this formula repeatedly to get, dropping the $f(x)\,dx$ in the integrals for convenience,

$$\int_a^b = \int_a^{c_1} + \int_{c_1}^b = \int_a^{c_1} + \int_{c_1}^{c_2} + \int_{c_2}^b = \int_a^{c_1} + \int_{c_1}^{c_2} + \int_{c_2}^{c_3} + \int_{c_3}^b$$

$$= \dots = \int_a^{c_1} + \int_{c_1}^{c_2} + \int_{c_2}^{c_3} + \dots + \int_{c_{j-1}}^{c_j} + \int_c^b.$$

To each integral in the last sum we apply Theorem 4, and hence

$$\int_a^b f(x)\, dx = [F(c_1) - F(a)] + [F(c_2) - F(c_1)] + [F(c_3) - F(c_2)]$$

$$+ \ldots + [F(c_j) - F(c_{j-1})] + [F(b) - F(c_j)].$$

All the terms on the right side cancel except two, namely $-F(a)$ and $F(b)$. Thus the theorem is proved.

REMARK ON NOTATION. The notation

$$[F(x)]_a^b \quad \text{or} \quad [F(x)]_{x=a}^{x=b}$$

is often used to denote $F(b) - F(a)$.

EXAMPLE 1. Evaluate the integral

$$\int_5^7 x^3\, dx.$$

Solution. Here we have $f(x) = x^3$ and so we can take $F(x)$ to be $x^4/4$; hence we get

$$\int_5^7 x^3\, dx = \left[\frac{x^4}{4}\right] = \frac{2401}{4} - \frac{625}{4} = 444.$$

Note that $f(x) = x^3$ is piecewise monotonic, in fact monotonic increasing, on the interval from $x = 3$ to $x = 7$, so that we are justified in using Theorem 5.

EXAMPLE 2. Evaluate the integral

$$\int_0^{\pi/2} \cos x\, dx.$$

Solution. In this case $f(x) = \cos x$ and we can take $F(x)$ to be $\sin x$. Hence we have

$$\int_0^{\pi/2} \cos x\, dx = [\sin x]_0^{\pi/2} = \sin\frac{\pi}{2} - \sin 0 = 1 - 0 = 1.$$

Note that $f(x) = \cos x$ is piecewise monotonic, in fact monotonic decreasing from $x = 0$ to $x = \pi/2$.

Thus Theorem 5, as these examples show, enables us to evaluate the integral of a function $f(x)$ if we can find a corresponding function $F(x)$ whose derivative is $f(x)$. This procedure is much briefer than the method of evaluating integrals given in Chapter 3. Take $\int_a^b \sin x\, dx$ for example, which was evaluated in § 3.6. Interpreting $f(x)$ as $\sin x$ in order to use Theorem 5, we seek a function $F(x)$ whose derivative is $\sin x$. Now we know from Chapter 4 that the derivative of $\cos x$ is $-\sin x$, and so the derivative of $-\cos x$ is $\sin x$. Thus the function $F(x)$ we seek is $-\cos x$. With $F(x) = -\cos x$ it follows that $F(b) = -\cos b$ and $F(a) = -\cos a$. So an application of Theorem 5 gives

$$\int_a^b \sin x\, dx = F(b) - F(a) = -\cos b - (-\cos a) = \cos a - \cos b.$$

It should be noted that $\sin x$ is a piecewise monotonic function on any finite interval from a to b, as required for an application of Theorem 5.

If this procedure for integrating $\sin x$ is compared with that in § 3.6, the strength of the fundamental theorem of calculus is readily observed. As another example of this strength we next consider the integral of x^n, another piecewise monotonic function.

It was established in Theorem 7 of § 4.3 that for any rational number n the derivative of x^n is nx^{n-1}. Replacing n by $n+1$ this gives

$$\frac{d}{dx}[x^{n+1}] = (n+1)x^n \quad \text{and} \quad \frac{d}{dx}[x^{n+1}/n+1] = x^n.$$

The second of these equations does not hold if $n = -1$ because this would give a zero denominator. Using Theorem 5 with

$$F(x) = \frac{x^{n+1}}{n+1} \quad \text{and} \quad f(x) = x^n,$$

we conclude that

$$\int_a^b x^n\, dx = \frac{b^{n+1}}{n+1} - \frac{a^{n+1}}{n+1}.$$

This is true for all real numbers n except $n = -1$, although the validity for irrational n is not justified until the end of § 7.3. The case $n = -1$, for which the formula is quite different, is treated in Theorem 6 of § 7.3.

Problems

1. Prove Theorems 1 and 2 of § 3.3 by use of Theorem 5 of the present section.

2. Prove Theorem 4 of § 3.6 by use of Theorem 5.

3. Verify the information given in Problem 1 in § 3.4.

4. Evaluate the following integrals.

(a) $\displaystyle\int_1^3 4x^3\,dx$ (h) $\displaystyle\int_0^{\pi/4} \cos x\,dx$

(b) $\displaystyle\int_2^4 x^3\,dx$ (i) $\displaystyle\int_0^{\pi/6} \cos x\,dx$

(c) $\displaystyle\int_0^2 (x^3 - x)\,dx$ (j) $\displaystyle\int_0^{\pi} \sin x\,dx$

(d) $\displaystyle\int_1^2 \frac{dx}{x^2}$ (k) $\displaystyle\int_{\pi/2}^{\pi} \sin x\,dx$

(e) $\displaystyle\int_1^3 \frac{x^3+1}{x^2}\,dx$ (l) $\displaystyle\int_0^1 \frac{dx}{1+x^2}$

(f) $\displaystyle\int_2^3 \frac{2\,dx}{x^3}$ (m) $\displaystyle\int_0^{\sqrt{3}/3} \frac{dx}{1+x^2}$

(g) $\displaystyle\int_0^{\pi/2} \cos x\,dx$ (n) $\displaystyle\int_0^1 \frac{2+x^2}{1+x^2}\,dx$

5. Evaluate the integrals

(a) $\displaystyle\int_0^1 \sqrt{x}\,dx$ (b) $\displaystyle\int_1^4 x^{-1/2}\,dx$

6. Evaluate the integrals

(a) $\displaystyle\int_0^1 x\sqrt{x^2+3}\,dx$ (b) $\displaystyle\int_0^1 x^2\sqrt{x^3+3}\,dx$

Suggestion for part (a): Check the derivative of $(x^2+3)^{3/2}$.

7. Find the numerical values of

(a) $\displaystyle\int_0^1 (x^2-2)^2\,dx$ (b) $\displaystyle\int_0^{\pi/4} \cos x\,dx$

(c) $\displaystyle\int_3^4 x^{-2}\,dx$ (d) $\displaystyle\int_0^{\pi/4} \sec^2 x\,dx$

8. Evaluate the following integrals, and *then* check your answers against the formulas in § 5.6:

(a) $\displaystyle\int_a^b \cos x\,dx$ (b) $\displaystyle\int_a^b \sec^2 x\,dx$, $-\dfrac{\pi}{2} < a < \dfrac{\pi}{2}$, $-\dfrac{\pi}{2} < b < \dfrac{\pi}{2}$

(c) $\displaystyle\int_a^b \frac{dx}{x^2+1}$ (d) $\displaystyle\int_a^b \frac{dx}{x^2+c^2}$, $c \neq 0$

Suggestion: Apply the fundamental theorem (Theorem 5) to the appropriate formulas in § 4.11, and for part (d) examine the derivative of arc tan x/c.

5.4 The Indefinite Integral. In applying Theorem 5, we have seen that the first question to be faced is to find a function $F(x)$ whose derivative is the integrand $f(x)$. For example, in evaluating the integral

$$\int_3^4 6x^5 \, dx$$

we look for a function $F(x)$ whose derivative is $6x^5$. The function x^6 will serve as $F(x)$, but so will x^6+3, x^6-5, and in general x^6+c, where c is any constant. Are there any other functions that will serve as $F(x)$? The answer is no, as the next two theorems show.

THEOREM 6. *Let $H(x)$ be a differentiable function whose derivative $H'(x) = 0$ on an interval $\alpha \leq x \leq \beta$. Then $H(x) = c$ on the interval, where c is some constant.*

Intuitively this seems plausible, because $H'(x) = 0$ implies that the slope of the curve $y = H(x)$ is zero, so that the curve has everywhere a horizontal tangent line. This suggests that $y = H(x)$ is a straight line parallel to the x-axis, i.e. $H(x) = c$.

PROOF. By the mean value theorem of § 4.7, with $f(x)$ and $F(x)$ now replaced by $H'(x)$ and $H(x)$, we see that given any two values $x = a$ and $x = b$ in the interval $\alpha \leq x \leq \beta$, then for some value k between a and b

$$H(b) - H(a) = (b-a)H'(k) = 0, \quad \text{or} \quad H(b) = H(a).$$

Thus $H(x)$ has the same value for all numbers x in the interval $\alpha \leq x \leq \beta$, so that $H(x) = c$.

THEOREM 7. *Let $F(x)$ and $G(x)$ be differentiable functions with equal derivatives on an interval $a \leq x \leq b$. Then $F(x) = G(x)+c$ on the interval, where c is some constant.*

PROOF. Write $H(x)$ for $F(x)-G(x)$, so that by Theorem 4 of § 4.3

$$H'(x) = F'(x) - G'(x) = 0.$$

Hence we can apply Theorem 6 to get

$$H(x) = c, \quad F(x) - G(x) = c, \quad F(x) = G(x)+c.$$

Having proved Theorem 7, we see that it justifies our remark just before Theorem 6 that x^6+c is the most general function whose derivative is $6x^5$. We call x^6+c the antiderivative or the indefinite integral of $6x^5$, and we write

$$\int 6x^5 \, dx \;=\; x^6 + c.$$

More generally, if the derivative of $F(x)$ is $f(x)$, we write

$$\int f(x) \, dx \;=\; F(x) + c,$$

and this is called the indefinite integral or the antiderivative of $f(x)$.

EXAMPLE. Evaluate the indefinite integral

$$\int (x^4 + x^2) \, dx.$$

Solution. Since we know that

$$\frac{d}{dx}(x^5) \;=\; 5x^4 \quad \text{and} \quad \frac{d}{dx}(x^3) \;=\; 3x^2,$$

we see that

$$\int (x^4 + x^2) \, dx \;=\; \frac{1}{5}x^5 + \frac{1}{3}x^3 + c.$$

Problems

Evaluate the following indefinite integrals.

1. $\displaystyle\int x \, dx$

2. $\displaystyle\int 3x^2 \, dx$

3. $\displaystyle\int (4x - 6x^2) \, dx$

4. $\displaystyle\int \frac{dx}{x^2}$

5. $\displaystyle\int \frac{dx}{x^3}$

6. $\displaystyle\int \frac{dx}{x^4}$

7. $\displaystyle\int \frac{dx}{1 + x^2}$

8. $\displaystyle\int \frac{dx}{2 + 2x^2}$

9. $\displaystyle\int \sin x \, dx$

10. $\displaystyle\int \cos x \, dx$

11. $\displaystyle\int \sin 2x \, dx$

12. $\displaystyle\int \cos 3x \, dx$

13. Evaluate the integrals

(a) $\displaystyle\int \sqrt{x}\,dx$ (c) $\displaystyle\int x^{-3}\,dx$

(b) $\displaystyle\int x^{2/3}\,dx$ (d) $\displaystyle\int (x^3+x)^2\,dx$

14. Prove that the most general function satisfying $dy/dx = x$ is $y = \frac{1}{2}x^2 + c$, where c is an arbitrary constant. Suggestion: Use Theorem 7 of § 5.4.

15. Find the most general solution of the equations:

(a) $\dfrac{dy}{dx} = x^3$ (b) $\dfrac{dy}{dx} = 2 \cos x.$

16. Let $F(x)$ and $G(x)$ be functions having the same derivative, say $f(x)$, on the interval $a \leq x \leq b$. Let $f(x)$ be piecewise monotonic on this interval. Give two proofs that $F(b)-F(a) = G(b)-G(a)$, one by using Theorem 5 of § 5.3, the other by using Theorem 7 of § 5.4.

5.5 Inequalities for integrals. The following results are needed for subsequent work with integrals.

THEOREM 8. *If two integrable functions* $F(x)$ *and* $G(x)$ *satisfy the inequality* $F(x) \leq G(x)$ *for all values of* x *on an interval* $a \leq x \leq b$, *then*

$$\int_a^b F(x)\,dx \leq \int_a^b G(x)\,dx.$$

From a geometric standpoint this theorem has a simple interpretation in case $F(x) \geq 0$. As shown in Figure 5.2 it asserts that the area

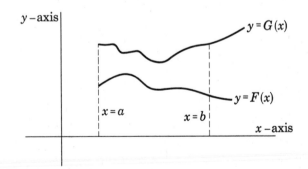

FIG. 5.2

between $y = G(x)$ and the x-axis is at least as large as the area between $F(x)$ and the x-axis, both taken from $x = a$ to $x = b$.

PROOF. Define the function $f(x)$ as the difference $F(x) - G(x)$, so that $f(x) \leq 0$ for all x in the interval $a \leq x \leq b$. Then by equation (8) of § 5.3, we see that if we write

$$\sigma_n = \sum_{j=1}^{n} (x_j - x_{j-1}) f(\xi_j),$$

then

$$\int_a^b f(x)\, dx = \lim_{n \to \infty} \sigma_n.$$

Furthermore since $x_j - x_{j-1} \geq 0$ and $f(\xi_j) \leq 0$ we see that $\sigma_n \leq 0$, and so by Theorem 15 of § 2.4

$$\int_a^b f(x)\, dx \leq 0.$$

But $f(x) = F(x) - G(x)$, and we apply Theorem 3 of § 3.5 to get

$$\int_a^b [F(x) - G(x)]\, dx = \int_a^b F(x)\, dx - \int_a^b G(x)\, dx \leq 0,$$

and

$$\int_a^b F(x)\, dx \leq \int_a^b G(x)\, dx.$$

THEOREM 9. *Let $f(x)$ be an integrable function on the interval $a \leq x \leq b$. Furthermore, let m and M be constants such that $m \leq f(x) \leq M$ over the interval. Then*

$$m(b-a) \leq \int_a^b f(x)\, dx \leq M(b-a).$$

This result has a simple geometric intepretation if $f(x) \geq 0$, illustrated in Figure 5.3, that the area bounded by the curve $y = f(x)$ and the

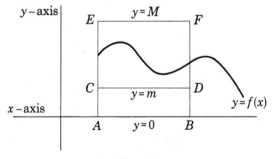

FIG. 5.3

x-axis, from $x = a$ to $x = b$, lies between the areas of the two rectangles ABDC and ABFE.

PROOF. First we apply Theorem 8 with $F(x)$ replaced by m, and $G(x)$ replaced by $f(x)$ to get

$$\int_a^b m \, dx \leqq \int_a^b f(x) \, dx, \quad \text{i.e.} \quad m(b-a) \leqq \int_a^b f(x) \, dx.$$

Next we apply Theorem 8 with $F(x)$ replaced by $f(x)$ and $G(x)$ replaced by M to get

$$\int_a^b f(x) \, dx \leqq \int_a^b M \, dx, \quad \text{i.e.} \quad \int_a^b f(x) \, dx \leqq M(b-a).$$

Problems

1. Prove that $2(b^3 - a^3) \geq 3(b^2 - a^2)$ for any numbers a and b satisfying $b \geq a \geq 1$. Suggestion: Apply Theorem 8 with $F(x) = x$, $G(x) = x^2$.

2. Prove that $3(b^4 - a^4) \geq 4(b^3 - a^3)$ for any numbers a and b satisfying $b \geq a \geq 1$.

3. Prove that $b^6 - a^6 \geq 3(b^2 - a^2)$ for any numbers a and b satisfying $b \geq a \geq 1$.

4. Compute $b - a$ and the best possible values of m and M as in Theorem 9 for the following integrals.

(a) $\int_1^2 \dfrac{dx}{x}$

(b) $\int_3^5 \dfrac{dx}{1+x}$

(c) $\int_2^4 \dfrac{dx}{x^2}$

(d) $\int_{-1}^1 x^2 \, dx$

(e) $\int_{\pi/6}^{\pi/3} \sin x \, dx$

(f) $\int_{\pi/6}^{\pi/3} \tan x \, dx$

(g) $\int_0^{\pi/2} \cos x \, dx$

(h) $\int_0^{\pi/2} (\sin x + \cos x) \, dx$

5.6 Summary of Formulas. The fundamental theorem of calculus states that if $(d/dx) F(x) = f(x)$, then $\int_a^b f(x) \, dx = F(b) - F(a)$; see Theorem 5 for restrictions on the use of this result.

$$\int_a^b x^n \, dx = \frac{b^{n+1} - a^{n+1}}{n+1}, \quad n \neq -1$$

$$\int_a^b \sin x \, dx = \cos a - \cos b \qquad \int_a^b \cos x \, dx = \sin b - \sin a$$

$$\int_a^b \sec^2 x \, dx = \tan b - \tan a, \qquad -\frac{\pi}{2} < a < \frac{\pi}{2}, \qquad -\frac{\pi}{2} < b < \frac{\pi}{2}$$

$$\int_a^b \frac{dx}{x^2 + c^2} = \frac{1}{c}\arctan\frac{b}{c} - \frac{1}{c}\arctan\frac{a}{c}, \quad c \neq 0$$

CHAPTER 6

THE TRIGONOMETRIC FUNCTIONS

6.0. The purpose of this chapter is to obtain infinite series expansions for the functions $\sin x$ and $\cos x$. To avoid a protracted discussion of the general theory of infinite series, we get at these expansions by a procedure involving inequalities. By our approach we gain brevity, but this is achieved by confining attention to a limited class of functions. As an application of the results, the computation of trigonometric tables is discussed.

6.1 Two Important Limits. As a preliminary, we first want to establish that for any positive integer n and any positive number β,

$$(1) \qquad (1+\beta)^n > n\beta.$$

This is a consequence of the binomial expansion, according to which

$$(1+\beta)^n = 1 + n\beta + \frac{n(n-1)}{2}\beta^2 + \frac{n(n-1)(n-2)}{6}\beta^3 + \cdots + \beta^n.$$

Since every term here is positive, the inequality (1) follows if we simply discard all terms except $n\beta$.

THEOREM 1. *Ler r be any real number strictly between -1 and $+1$, that is $-1 < r < 1$. Then*

$$\lim_{n\to\infty} r^n = 0.$$

PROOF. Consider first the case where r is positive. For any positive number ϵ, we must prove that $r^n < \epsilon$ for all but a finite number of integers n. Since $r < 1$, there is a positive number β such that $r = 1/(1+\beta)$. In fact, by solving this equation we see that

$$\beta = \frac{1-r}{r},$$

and this is clearly positive. Then from (1) we see that

$$(2) \qquad r^n = \frac{1}{(1+\beta)^n} < \frac{1}{n\beta},$$

by using Theorem 6 of § 2.1. Now for any given ϵ the relation $(1/n\beta) < \epsilon$ holds for all but a finite number of positive integers n; in fact it holds for all integers n exceeding $1/(\beta\epsilon)$. So by (2) we see that $r^n < \epsilon$ holds for all but a finite number of positive integers n.

Passing over the case $r = 0$, suppose now that $r < 0$. The same proof as above holds with r replaced by $|r|$, so that $|r^n| < \epsilon$ holds for all but a finite number of positive integers.

The next theorem contains the notation $n!$, read "n factorial", which denotes for any positive integer n the product of all positive integers from 1 to n, thus

$$n! = n(n-1)(n-2) \cdots 3 \cdot 2 \cdot 1.$$

THEOREM 2. *For any constant c,*

$$\lim_{n\to\infty} \frac{c^n}{n!} = 0.$$

PROOF. As in Theorem 1 we prove this for $c > 0$, and the result then follows in case $c < 0$ by the definition of limit of a sequence in § 2.3. Define k as the least integer satisfying $k > 2c$, so that k is fixed. Writing $k+m$ for n we see that

$$\frac{c^n}{n!} = \frac{c^{k+m}}{(k+m)!} = \frac{c^k}{k!} \cdot \frac{c}{k+1} \cdot \frac{c}{k+2} \cdot \frac{c}{k+3} \cdots \frac{c}{k+m}.$$

Now $c^k/k!$ is a constant, say C, and each of the other factors $c/(k+1)$, $c/(k+2)$, ..., $c/(k+m)$ is less than $\frac{1}{2}$. Hence we have

$$\frac{c^n}{n!} < C\left(\frac{1}{2}\right)^m.$$

As n tends to infinity, so does m, and so we see that

$$\lim\left(\frac{1}{2}\right)^m = 0, \quad \lim C\left(\frac{1}{2}\right)^m = 0, \quad \lim\frac{c^n}{n!} = 0,$$

by applying Theorem 1 of the present section, Theorem 11 of § 2.4, and Theorem 9 of § 2.3.

Finally we prove a result about subsequences: a subsequence of a sequence $a_1, a_2, a_3, \ldots$ is any partial set of the terms, as for example $a_4, a_8, a_{12}, a_{16}, \ldots$.

THEOREM 3. *If an infinite sequence $\{a_n\}$ tends to a limit a, so does any infinite subsequence*

PROOF. Let ϵ be any given positive number. By definition, all except a finite number of the inequalities

$$- \epsilon < a_n - a < \epsilon, \quad n = 1, 2, 3, \ldots ,$$

hold. It follows *a fortiori* that these inequalities are satisfied by all but a finite number of terms of the subsequence.

Problems

1. Prove inequality (1) by using Theorem 8 of § 5.5 with $F(x) = 1$, $G(x) = (1+x)^{n-1}$, $a = 0$, $b = \beta$.

2. Find the following limits:

(a) $\lim_{n \to \infty} \dfrac{2^n}{(n+1)!}$

(b) $\lim_{n \to \infty} \dfrac{n! + 3^n}{n!}$

(c) $\lim_{n \to \infty} \dfrac{n!}{(n+1)!}$

(d) $\lim_{n \to \infty} \dfrac{5^n 6^{n+1}}{n!}$

(e) $\lim_{n \to \infty} 8(4/5)^n$

(f) $\lim_{n \to \infty} \dfrac{n!}{(2n)!}$

(g) $\lim_{n \to \infty} \dfrac{(2n)! - n!}{(2n)!}$

3. Prove that inequality (1) in the text is true for every integer n and every non-negative number β.

4. If n is an integer, prove that $2^n > n$.

5. Prove that $y^n > ny$ for every positive integer $n \geq 2$ and every real number $y > 2$.

6. For every positive integer $n \geq 2$ and every positive number β, prove that $(1 + \beta)^n > \beta^n + n\beta^{n-1}$.

6.2 Infinite Series Expansions for sin x and cos x. We begin with the inequality $\cos x \leq 1$, which holds for all values of x. By applying Theorem 8 of § 5.5, with $F(x)$ and $G(x)$ replaced by $\cos x$ and 1, we conclude that

$$(3) \qquad \int_0^t \cos x \, dx \leq \int_0^t 1 \, dx$$

for any positive number t. Since the derivative of $\sin x$ is $\cos x$, and since $\sin 0 = 0$, the integral on the left side of (3) equals $\sin t$, and so (3) states that $\sin t \leq t$. This holds for any positive value of t, so we can apply Theorem 8 of § 5.5 with $F(x)$ and $G(x)$ replaced by $\sin x$ and x; thus

$$\int_0^t \sin x \, dx \leq \int_0^t x \, dx$$

for any positive number t. Since the derivative of $\cos x$ is $-\sin x$, the evaluation of these integrals gives

$$1 - \cos t \leq \frac{t^2}{2} \quad \text{or} \quad 1 - \frac{t^2}{2} \leq \cos t.$$

Consequently we can apply Theorem 8 of § 5.5 with $F(x)$ and $G(x)$ replaced by $1 - x^2/2$ and $\cos x$, to get

$$\int_0^t \left(1 - \frac{x^2}{2}\right) dx \leq \int_0^t \cos x \, dx.$$

Integrating, we find that

$$t - \frac{t^3}{3!} \leq \sin t$$

for any positive number t. The repetition of this process leads to a series of inequalities which are valid for any positive number x:

$$(4) \begin{cases}
\cos x \leq 1 & \sin x \leq x \\[2mm]
\cos x \geq 1 - \dfrac{x^2}{2!} & \sin x \geq x - \dfrac{x^3}{3!} \\[2mm]
\cos x \leq 1 - \dfrac{x^2}{2!} + \dfrac{x^4}{4!} & \sin x \leq x - \dfrac{x^3}{3!} + \dfrac{x^5}{5!} \\[2mm]
\cos x \geq 1 - \dfrac{x^2}{2!} + \dfrac{x^4}{4!} - \dfrac{x^6}{6!} & \sin x \geq x - \dfrac{x^3}{3!} + \dfrac{x^5}{5!} - \dfrac{x^7}{7!}
\end{cases}$$

etc.

Let us look first at the inequalities for $\cos x$. We define $a_1, a_2, a_3, \ldots$ by the equations

$$a_1 = 1, \quad a_2 = 1 - \frac{x^2}{2!} + \frac{x^4}{4!}, \quad a_3 = 1 - \frac{x^2}{2!} + \frac{x^4}{4!} - \frac{x^6}{6!} + \frac{x^8}{8!},$$

$$a_4 = 1 - \frac{x^2}{2!} + \frac{x^4}{4!} - \frac{x^6}{6!} + \frac{x^8}{8!} - \frac{x^{10}}{10!} + \frac{x^{12}}{12!},$$

and in general

$$a_n = 1 - \frac{x^2}{2!} + \frac{x^4}{4!} - \frac{x^6}{6!} + \ldots - \frac{x^{4n-6}}{(4n-6)!} + \frac{x^{4n-4}}{(4n-4)!}.$$

Similarly we define $b_1, b_2, b_3, \ldots$ by the equations

$$b_1 = 1 - \frac{x^2}{2!}, \quad b_2 = 1 - \frac{x^2}{2!} + \frac{x^4}{4!} - \frac{x^6}{6!},$$

$$b_3 = 1 - \frac{x^2}{2!} + \frac{x^4}{4!} - \frac{x^6}{6!} + \frac{x^8}{8!} - \frac{x^{10}}{10!},$$

$$b_4 = 1 - \frac{x^2}{2!} + \frac{x^4}{4!} - \frac{x^6}{6!} + \frac{x^8}{8!} - \frac{x^{10}}{10!} + \frac{x^{12}}{12!} - \frac{x^{14}}{14!},$$

and in general

$$b_n = 1 - \frac{x^2}{2!} + \frac{x^4}{4!} - \frac{x^6}{6!} + \ldots + \frac{x^{4n-4}}{(4n-4)!} - \frac{x^{4n-2}}{(4n-2)!}.$$

With these definitions we see that the inequalities on $\cos x$ can be written in the following form:

$$(5) \quad \begin{cases} \cos x \leqq a_1 & \cos x \geqq b_1 \\ \cos x \leqq a_2 & \cos x \geqq b_2 \\ \cos x \leqq a_3 & \cos x \geqq b_3 \\ \cos x \leqq a_4 & \cos x \geqq b_4 \end{cases}$$

etc.

Let us think of x as a fixed positive number. Then we can apply Theorem 14 of § 2.4, because

$$a_n - b_n = \frac{x^{4n-2}}{(4n-2)!}, \quad \lim_{n \to \infty}(a_n - b_n) = \lim \frac{x^{4n-2}}{(4n-2)!} = 0$$

by Theorems 2 and 3 of § 6.1. The conclusion is that $a_n \to \cos x$ and $b_n \to \cos x$, so that $\cos x$ is expressible as an infinite series

$$(6) \qquad \cos x = 1 - \frac{x^2}{2!} + \frac{x^4}{4!} - \frac{x^6}{6!} + \frac{x^8}{8!} - \ldots.$$

A similar argument can be applied to those inequalities (4) involving $\sin x$, to give the result

$$(7) \qquad \sin x = x - \frac{x^3}{3!} + \frac{x^5}{5!} - \frac{x^7}{7!} + \frac{x^9}{9!} - \ldots.$$

Equations (6) and (7) have been established only for positive values of x. However, it is easy to see that they must be valid for all values of x, positive, negative, or zero. Let us begin with (6). If $x = 0$, equation (6) states that $\cos 0 = 1$, which is correct. For negative values of x, we recall from trigonometry that $\cos(-x) = \cos x$, and we note that the right side of equation (6) has this same property, that it is unchanged when x is replaced by $-x$, because

$$(-x)^2 = x^2, \quad (-x)^4 = x^4, \quad (-x)^6 = x^6, \text{ etc.}$$

Hence equation (6) holds for every real number x.

As for equation (7), it becomes the well-known result $\sin 0 = 0$ when x is replaced by zero. For negative x, we know that $\sin(-x) = -\sin x$, and the right side of equation (7) also changes sign when x is replaced by $-x$, because

$$(-x)^3 = -x^3, \quad (-x)^5 = -x^5, \quad (-x)^7 = -x^7, \text{ etc.}$$

Equations (6) and (7) are thus seen to be valid for all real numbers x, where of course x must be taken in radian measure. The reason for this is that all our formulas and theorems about the differentiation and integration of $\sin x$ and $\cos x$ were based on radian measure. However, for an angle measured in degrees, equations (6) and (7) can be applied by first converting the angle into radian measure.

EXAMPLE. Evaluate $\cos \frac{1}{5}$ with accuracy to five decimal places.
Solution. Using equation (6) we see that

$$\cos \frac{1}{5} = 1 - \frac{1}{2}\left(\frac{1}{5}\right)^2 + \frac{1}{4!}\left(\frac{1}{5}\right)^4 - \ldots \cong .98007,$$

where the symbol $\cong$ stands for "is approximately equal to".

The approximate value .98007 of $\cos \frac{1}{5}$ has been obtained here by using only the first three terms of the series. How can we be certain that .98007 is accurate to five decimal places? Might it not be that the rest of the terms in the infinite series have influence in determining the first five decimal places? The answer to this question is no, as the following analysis will demonstrate.

When an approximation a is used in place of a number α, we shall say that the error is $|a - \alpha|$. For example, if the number is 22.9 and the approximation is 23, the error is .1. Similarly, if the number is 23.1 and the approximation is 23, the error is .1. Thus for our purposes we are making no distinction between approximations larger than and those smaller than the number.

THEOREM 4. *If the first k terms of the series* (6) *are used to compute an approximation to* $\cos x$, *then the error is at most the absolute value of the $k + 1$-st term.* An analogous result holds for equation (7).

Before proving this in general, let us begin with the example above. In view of the inequalities (5), we can conclude that

$$1 - \frac{1}{2}\left(\frac{1}{5}\right)^2 + \frac{1}{4!}\left(\frac{1}{5}\right)^4 - \frac{1}{6!}\left(\frac{1}{5}\right)^6 \leqq \cos\frac{1}{5} \leqq 1 - \frac{1}{2}\left(\frac{1}{5}\right)^2 + \frac{1}{4!}\left(\frac{1}{5}\right)^4,$$

or, in abbreviated notation, $b_2 \leqq \cos \frac{1}{5} \leqq a_2$. Thus $\cos \frac{1}{5}$ lies between b_2 and a_2, two numbers whose difference is

$$(8) \qquad \frac{1}{6!}\left(\frac{1}{5}\right)^6 \cong .00000009.$$

Now if a_2 is used as an approximation to $\cos \frac{1}{5}$, the error is $a_2 - \cos \frac{1}{5}$, and this is at most $a_2 - b_2$. That is, the error is at most the number (8) above. Thus we are certain that the approximation .98007 to $\cos \frac{1}{5}$, obtained by using the first five decimal places of a_2, is accurate to five decimal places.

The proof of Theorem 4 in general is virtually the same. It is based on the simple idea that if $\cos x$ lies between two approximations a and A, the error in using either approximation is at most $|A - a|$. We note that in view of (4), $\cos x$ lies between the sum of the first k terms of (6), namely,

$$(9) \qquad 1 - \frac{x^2}{2!} + \frac{x^4}{4!} - \frac{x^6}{6!} + \ldots + (-1)^{k-1}\frac{x^{2k-2}}{(2k-2)!},$$

and the sum of the first $k + 1$ terms, namely,

$$1 - \frac{x^2}{2!} + \frac{x^4}{4!} - \frac{x^6}{6!} + \ldots + (-1)^{k-1}\frac{x^{2k-2}}{(2k-2)!} + (-1)^k\frac{x^{2k}}{(2k)!}.$$

Hence the error in using (9) as an approximation to $\cos x$ is at most the absolute value of the difference between these sums, namely

$$\left|(-1)^k\frac{x^{2k}}{(2k)!}\right| = \left|\frac{x^{2k}}{(2k)!}\right|.$$

This is the absolute value of the $k + 1$-st term of the series (6), and so Theorem 4 is proved.

Problems

1. Compute $\sin \frac{1}{5}$ to 5 decimal places of accuracy.

2. Compute $\sin 2°$ to 5 decimal places of accuracy. Suggestion: The angle $2°$ becomes $\pi/90$ when converted to radians. Use $\pi = 3.14159$.

3. Compute $\sin 87°$ to 5 decimal places of accuracy. Suggestion: $\sin 87°$ $= \cos 3°$.

4. Compute $\cos 86°$ to 5 decimal places of accuracy.

5. Presuming that it is correct to differentiate an infinite series term by term (which it is in this case), differentiate equation (7) to get (6).

6. Verify that when (6) is differentiated term by term the result is (7) with all signs changed.

7. Replace x by $2x$ in every term in (7) to get an infinite series expansion for $\sin 2x$. Then verify as far as powers up to x^7 that this is the same as $2 \sin x \cos x$ by multiplying equations (6) and (7).

8. Compute a series expansion for $\sin^2 x$ as far as powers up to x^8 by replacing x by $2x$ in (6) and using the identity $\cos 2x = 1 - 2 \sin^2 x$.

9. Compute a series expansion for $\cos^2 x$ as far as powers up to x^8.

10. Compute a series for $\sin^3 x$ as far as powers up to x^7 by using the identity $\sin 3x = 3 \sin x - 4 \sin^3 x$.

6.3 Remarks on Infinite Series.

The series expansions of $\cos x$ and $\sin x$ in (6) and (7) are special cases of what are called Taylor series. These are series which give an alternative form of a function $f(x)$,

$$(10) \qquad f(x) = k_0 + k_1 x + k_2 x^2 + k_3 x^3 + \ldots ,$$

in the same sense that $1 + 2x + x^2$ is another form of the function $(1+x)^2$. Only a restricted class of functions $f(x)$ can be expanded into a series of the form (10). We do not discuss here the restrictions on $f(x)$, nor do we deal with the question of how the coefficients k_0, k_1, k_2, ... can be determined from $f(x)$.

We shall get the Taylor series expansions for several functions, but as in the cases of $\cos x$ and $\sin x$, we shall use special methods to obtain the series. From the manner in which we get the series, there will be no need to discuss fully what is called "convergence" and "divergence" of series. But we shall make a few remarks about this important topic.

To begin with a couple of examples, the series

$$.3 + .03 + .003 + .0003 + \ldots$$

is convergent. It converges to the limit $\frac{1}{3}$. On the other hand the series

$$1 + 1 + 1 + 1 + 1 + 1 + \ldots$$

is not convergent; it is divergent. In general, the sum of an infinite series of terms

$$(11) \qquad a_1 + a_2 + a_3 + a_4 + \ldots$$

is said to be convergent if the sequence of "partial sums" $s_1, s_2, s_3, s_4, \ldots$

tends to a limit, where the partial sums are defined by the equations

$$s_1 = a_1, \quad s_2 = a_1 + a_2, \quad s_3 = a_1 + a_2 + a_3,$$

$$\ldots, s_n = \sum_{j=1}^{n} a_j.$$

Each of the terms $a_1, a_2, a_3, \ldots$ may be positive, negative, or zero. If the partial sums $s_1, s_2, s_3, \ldots$ tend to a limit s, then the series (11) is said to converge to s.

In § 6.2 we used the theory of limits as developed in Chapter 2 in establishing equations (6) and (7). The approach that we took assures us that the series in (6) and (7) are convergent for every value of x, positive, negative or zero.

6.4 Summary of Formulas. With x in radian measure:

$$\sin x = x - \frac{x^3}{3!} + \frac{x^5}{5!} - \frac{x^7}{7!} + \frac{x^9}{9!} - \ldots$$

$$\cos x = 1 - \frac{x^2}{2!} + \frac{x^4}{4!} - \frac{x^6}{6!} + \frac{x^8}{8!} - \ldots$$

CHAPTER 7

THE LOGARITHMIC AND EXPONENTIAL FUNCTIONS

7.0. What was done in the preceding chapter for trigonometric functions is now done for logarithmic and exponential functions, specifically for $y = \log x$ and $y = e^x$. The number e is a fundamental mathematical constant whose nature and properties will be revealed in the subsequent discussion.

It might have been noted that in our treatment of differentiation in Chapter 4, the derivatives of various trigonometric functions were obtained, but no derivatives of exponential or logarithmic functions. Such derivatives are more difficult, and in order to get at them, we shall start by defining the logarithmic function in terms of an integral. But because the reader is already familiar with $\log x$ defined in another way, and because it is not apparent that these definitions amount to the same thing, we shall call our function $L(x)$ at first. Later in the discussion it will become clear that $L(x)$ is the logarithmic function, and then we shall change its label from $L(x)$ to $\log x$.

From a strict logical standpoint, the work of Appendix A should precede the present chapter, and the reader can take them in that order if he wishes. We have placed the existence proof in an appendix in order to break the theoretical development into smaller pieces, and to postpone the more difficult part of the theory.

7.1 A Function Defined. The equation

$$\int_1^b x^2 \, dx = \frac{b^3}{3} - \frac{1}{3}$$

is quite familiar; it is a special case of Theorem 1 of § 3.3. If we regard b as a variable quantity we see that the integral is a function of b, namely $(b^3 - 1)/3$. To change from b to the more standard variable x we can write

(1)
$$\int_1^x v^2\, dv = \frac{x^3}{3} - \frac{1}{3}.$$

This integral, then, is just another way of writing $(x^3 - 1)/3$. Geometrically, the integral signifies the area under the curve $y = v^2$, taken from $v = 1$ to $v = x$ as shown in Figure 7.1. The difference between this and previous areas is that we have no definite boundary on the right, since x can be any value we want to specify. It is understandable, then, that the integral (1) is a function of x, but not a function of v because v is merely a dummy variable of integration.

Now analogous to (1) we define a function of x, denoted by $L(x)$, by the equation

(2)
$$L(x) = \int_1^x \frac{dv}{v} = \int_1^x v^{-1}\, dv, \quad \text{for any } x > 0.$$

In case $x > 1$ this can be conceived* of as the area between the curve $y = 1/v$ and the v axis, taken from $v = 1$ to $v = x$. The restriction $x > 0$ is imposed in equation (2), and the graph in Figure 7.2 suggests

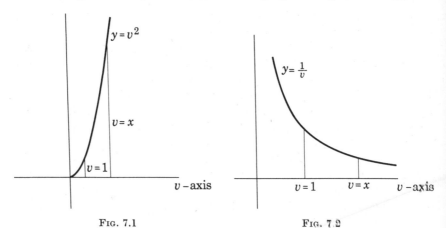

FIG. 7.1   FIG. 7.2

* The theorems on the existence of the integral $\int_a^b f(x)\, dx$ depended on our knowledge of a function $F(x)$ whose derivative is $f(x)$. In the present case the variable of integration is v, and $f(v) = v^{-1}$. But we have no knowledge of the existence of a function $F(v)$ whose derivative, with respect to v, is v^{-1}. Thus while we can conceive of some meaning for the integral (2) from a geometric picture, we are not certain of the existence of this integral because a careful development of calculus should not be based on geometric intuition. To avoid an unduly complicated analysis at this point, we postpone the proof of the existence of such integrals as (2) until Appendix A.

why. As v tends to 0 through positive values, the y values increase beyond all bound, so that y has no value when $v = 0$. Thus the limits of integration must not include $v = 0$, nor cross $v = 0$. Figure 7.2 illustrates the case $x > 1$, for which the function $L(x)$ has positive values. We note that

$$(3) \qquad L(1) = \int_1^1 \frac{dv}{v} = 0,$$

and $L(x)$ is negative for any x in the range $0 < x < 1$. These conclusions follow from the general definition of an integral in § 3.2.

THEOREM 1. *The derivative of $L(x)$ is $1/x$, i.e., $L'(x) = 1/x$.*

PROOF. By the definition of derivative

$$L'(x) = \lim_{\Delta x \to 0} \frac{L(x + \Delta x) - L(x)}{\Delta x} = \lim_{\Delta x \to 0} \frac{1}{\Delta x} \left\{ \int_1^{x+\Delta x} \frac{dv}{v} - \int_1^x \frac{dv}{v} \right\}.$$

From equation (5) of § 3.2 we see that the integrals can be combined, thus

$$L'(x) = \lim_{\Delta x \to 0} \left[\frac{1}{\Delta x} \int_x^{x+\Delta x} \frac{dv}{v} \right].$$

First let us consider the limit as Δx tends to zero through positive values. In this case we see that the integrand has maximum value $1/x$ on the range of integration, and minimum value $1/(x + \Delta x)$. Hence we can apply Theorem 9 of § 5.5. with a and b replaced by x and $x + \Delta x$, and we can take $m = 1/(x + \Delta x)$ and $M = 1/x$. Hence we get, since $b - a$ is replaced by Δx,

$$(4) \qquad \frac{\Delta x}{x + \Delta x} \leq \int_x^{x+\Delta x} \frac{dv}{v} \leq \frac{\Delta x}{x}.$$

Dividing through by Δx we get

$$(5) \qquad \frac{1}{x + \Delta x} \leq \frac{1}{\Delta x} \int_x^{x+\Delta x} \frac{dv}{v} \leq \frac{1}{x}.$$

As Δx tends to zero we see that the center term is caught between $1/x$ and a fraction which is tending to $1/x$. It follows that $L'(x) = 1/x$.

But what if Δx tends to zero through negative values? In this case we apply Theorem 9 of § 5.5 to the integral

$$\int_{x+\Delta x}^x \frac{dv}{v} \quad \text{with} \quad m = \frac{1}{x}, \quad M = \frac{1}{x + \Delta x}, \quad b - a = -\Delta x.$$

Thus we get, in place of (4),

$$\frac{-\Delta x}{x} \leqq \int_{x+\Delta x}^{x} \frac{dv}{v} \leqq \frac{-\Delta x}{x+\Delta x}.$$

We multiply by the positive quantity $-1/\Delta x$, and interchange the upper and lower limits on the integral; cf. Theorem 2 of § 2.1 and equation (6) of § 3.2. This gives

$$\frac{1}{x} \leqq \frac{1}{\Delta x} \int_{x}^{x+\Delta x} \frac{dv}{v} \leqq \frac{1}{x+\Delta x},$$

which is (5) with the inequalities reversed. As Δx tends to zero it follows again that $L'(x) = 1/x$.

From Theorem 1 we can easily get the fundamental property of the function $L(x)$, as follows.

THEOREM 2. *For any positive numbers a and x,*

$$L(ax) = L(a) + L(x).$$

The reader will notice that this resembles one of the basic properties of logarithms, namely $\log ab = \log a + \log b$. This resemblance does not entitle us, however, to say that the function $L(x)$ we are studying must be the logarithmic function. This identification will come later in the analysis.

PROOF. We will regard a as a constant, and we consider the derivative of $L(ax)$ with respect to x. We write u for ax and apply Theorem 11 of § 4.5 to $y = L(ax)$, thus

$$y = L(u), \quad u = ax, \quad \frac{dy}{du} = L'(u) = \frac{1}{u}, \quad \frac{du}{dx} = a,$$

$$\frac{d}{dx}\{L(ax)\} = \frac{dy}{dx} = \frac{dy}{du} \cdot \frac{du}{dx} = \frac{1}{u} \cdot a = \frac{1}{ax} \cdot a = \frac{1}{x}.$$

Thus we see that $L(x)$ and $L(ax)$ have the same derivative, namely $1/x$, and so by Theorem 7 of § 5.4 we conclude that $L(x)$ and $L(ax)$ differ by a constant,

(6) $$L(ax) = L(x) + c.$$

To determine the value of the constant, we set $x = 1$ and use equation (3) to get

$$L(a) = L(1) + c = 0 + c = c.$$

Thus $c = L(a)$, and substituting this in (6), we have proved Theorem 2.

Problems

1. Express $\int_2^5 (dx/x)$ in terms of the L function.
2. Prove that $L(a^2) = 2L(a)$, $L(a^3) = 3L(a)$ and $L(a^4) = 4L(a)$ for any positive number a.
3. Prove that $L(\frac{1}{2}) = -L(2)$. Suggestion: Substitute $a = \frac{1}{2}$ and $x = 2$ in Theorem 2.
4. Prove that $L(\frac{1}{3}) = -L(3)$.
5. Prove that $L(\frac{3}{4}) = -L(\frac{4}{3})$.
6. Prove that $L(6) + L(10) + L(15) = 2L(30)$.
7. Prove that

$$\int_1^4 \frac{dx}{x} + \int_1^5 \frac{dx}{x} = \int_1^{20} \frac{dx}{x}.$$

8. Combine the sum

$$\int_1^3 \frac{dx}{x} + \int_1^5 \frac{dx}{x}$$

into a single integral.
9. Combine the sum

$$\int_1^3 \frac{dx}{x} + \int_1^6 \frac{dx}{x} + \int_1^{\frac{1}{2}} \frac{dx}{x}$$

into a single integral.
10. Prove that $L(1/b) = -L(b)$ for every positive number b. Suggestion: set $a = b$ and $x = 1/b$ in Theorem 2.
11. For all positive numbers a and b prove that $L(a/b) = L(a) - L(b)$.
12. For every positive number b prove that $L(\sqrt{b}) = \frac{1}{2}L(b)$.

7.2 Properties of $L(x)$. If we replace a and x by any positive numbers b_1 and b_2 in Theorem 2 we get

$$L(b_1 b_2) = L(b_1) + L(b_2).$$

If we replace a and x by $b_1 b_2$ and b_3, we see that

$$L(b_1 b_2 b_3) = L(b_1 b_2) + L(b_3) = L(b_1) + L(b_2) + L(b_3).$$

Next we can replace a and x by $b_1 b_2 b_3$ and b_4 to get

$$L(b_1 b_2 b_3 b_4) = L(b_1 b_2 b_3) + L(b_4) = L(b_1) + L(b_2) + L(b_3) + L(b_4).$$

Continuing in this fashion we see that for any positive numbers b_1, b_2, b_3, ..., b_n,

(7) $\qquad L(b_1 b_2 b_3 ... b_n) = L(b_1) + L(b_2) + L(b_3) + ... + L(b_n).$

If the numbers b_1, b_2, ..., b_n are all equal, say equal to b, we get

(8) $\qquad L(b^n) = L(b) + L(b) + L(b) + ... + L(b) = nL(b).$

For later use it will also be convenient to know that

(9) $$L(2) < 1, \quad L(3) > 1.$$

To prove the first of these we apply Theorem 9 of § 5.5 to

$$L(2) = \int_1^2 \frac{dv}{v} = \int_1^{3/2} \frac{dv}{v} + \int_{3/2}^2 \frac{dv}{v} = I_1 + I_2 \quad \text{(say)}.$$

With the integrand $1/v$, we can take $M = 1$ in I_1 and $M = \frac{2}{3}$ in I_2 and so we have

$$I_1 \leq 1\left(\frac{3}{2} - 1\right) = \frac{1}{2}, \quad I_2 \leq \frac{2}{3}\left(2 - \frac{3}{2}\right) = \frac{1}{3}, \quad L(2) \leq \frac{1}{2} + \frac{1}{3} = \frac{5}{6} < 1.$$

To prove the second part of (9) we do much the same thing, except that we apply the other part of Theorem 9 of § 5.5. It is necessary to break the integral into more parts; thus we take

$$L(3) = \int_1^3 \frac{dv}{v} = \int_1^{5/4} + \int_{5/4}^{3/2} + \int_{3/2}^{7/4} + \int_{7/4}^2 + \int_2^{5/2} + \int_{5/2}^3.$$

In the application of Theorem 9 of § 5.5 to these six integrals, we can take m to be $\frac{4}{5}, \frac{2}{3}, \frac{4}{7}, \frac{1}{2}, \frac{2}{5}$, and $\frac{1}{3}$ in the respective cases. Hence we can write

$$L(3) \geq \frac{4}{5}\left(\frac{5}{4} - 1\right) + \frac{2}{3}\left(\frac{3}{2} - \frac{5}{4}\right) + \frac{4}{7}\left(\frac{7}{4} - \frac{3}{2}\right) + \frac{1}{2}\left(2 - \frac{7}{4}\right)$$

$$+ \frac{2}{5}\left(\frac{5}{2} - 2\right) + \frac{1}{3}\left(3 - \frac{5}{2}\right),$$

$$L(3) \geq \frac{1}{5} + \frac{1}{6} + \frac{1}{7} + \frac{1}{8} + \frac{1}{5} + \frac{1}{6}.$$

It follows by a straightforward calculation that $L(3) > 1$.

From the definition (2) of $L(x)$, we can see that since the integrand $1/v$ is positive, the value of $L(x)$ increases as x increases, and decreases as x decreases. In other words, $L(x)$ is a monotonic increasing function. As x increases indefinitely, that is to say, as x tends to infinity, what happens to $L(x)$? The answer is that $L(x)$ also increases indefinitely as the following argument shows.

From equation (8) with $b = 3$, and from (9), we conclude that

$$L(3^n) = nL(3) > n.$$

Hence we can make $L(3^n)$ as large as we please by taking n sufficiently large. In other words, $L(3^n)$ increases indefinitely as n increases indefinitely, and so $L(x)$ tends to infinity with x.

The function $L(x)$ is defined for $x > 0$. What happens to $L(x)$ as x tends to zero? To answer this, we replace a and x in Theorem 2 by 3^n and 3^{-n}, and so by equation (3) we get

$$L(3^n \cdot 3^{-n}) = L(3^n) + L(3^{-n}), \quad L(3^n \cdot 3^{-n}) = L(1) = 0,$$

$$L(3^n) + L(3^{-n}) = 0, \quad L(3^{-n}) = -nL(3).$$

Thus as n increases indefinitely, $L(3^{-n})$ decreases indefinitely: as n tends to infinity, $L(3^{-n})$ tends to minus infinity. But as n tends to infinity, (3^{-n}) tends to zero. Thus we can write*

$$\lim_{n \to \infty} L(3^{-n}) = -\infty,$$

$$\lim_{x \to 0} L(x) = -\infty.$$

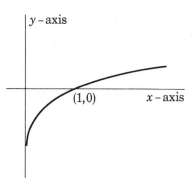

With this information about $L(x)$ we can make an approximate sketch of its graph. The function has a derivative, and so by Theorem 1 of § 4.1 it is continuous. The graph of the function is shown in Figure 7.3.

Fig. 7.3 Sketch of $y = L(x)$ or $y = \log x$.

Problems

1. Prove that $L(3) \leqq \frac{3}{2}$. Suggestion: Separate $\int_1^3$ into the parts $\int_1^2$ and $\int_2^3$.

2. Prove that $L(4) \leqq 1 + \frac{1}{2} + \frac{1}{3}$.

3. Prove that

$$L(n) \leqq 1 + \frac{1}{2} + \frac{1}{3} + \dots + \frac{1}{n-1}.$$

4. Prove that

$$L(n) \geqq \frac{1}{2} + \frac{1}{3} + \dots + \frac{1}{n-1} + \frac{1}{n}.$$

5. Prove that $L(\frac{1}{2}) > -1$.

6. Prove that $L(\frac{1}{3}) < -1$.

7. Prove that $L(\frac{5}{2}) \leqq 1$.

---

* In writing $\lim_{x \to 0} L(x) = -\infty$, our notation is somewhat at variance with our language about limits. If we ask the question, "Does the function $L(x)$ have a limit as x tends to zero?", the answer is "No". The reason is that in saying that a sequence or a function has a limit we mean a *finite* limit.

8. Prove that $L(c/b) = L(c) - L(b)$ for positive numbers c and b.

9. Prove that $L(\sqrt{c}) = \frac{1}{2}L(c)$ for $c > 0$.

10. Prove that $L(\sqrt[3]{c}) = \frac{1}{3}L(c)$ for $c > 0$.

11. Prove that $L(\sqrt[n]{c}) = (1/n)L(c)$ for any positive integer n, and $c > 0$.

12. Find the equation of the tangent line to $y = L(x)$ at the point $(1, 0)$.

7.3 The Exponential Function. Since the function $y = L(x)$ is monotonic increasing and differentiable, with $L'(x) \neq 0$ on the interval $0 < x < \infty$, we can apply Theorem 12 of § 4.6, and conclude that the inverse function is also differentiable. Denoting the inverse function by $x = E(y)$, we see by the same theorem that

$$L'(x) \cdot E'(y) = 1, \quad E'(y) = x,$$

since $L'(x) = 1/x$. Now $x = E(y)$ so we see that $E'(y) = E(y)$. Writing this with the usual variable x, we conclude that

$$(10) \qquad \frac{d}{dx}E(x) = E'(x) = E(x).$$

The graph of the equation $y = E(x)$ can be obtained at once from the graph of $y = L(x)$ in Figure 7.3 by interchanging the roles of x and y, as shown in Figure 7.4. Note that the domain of the function $y = E(x)$ is $-\infty < x < \infty$, and that $E(x) > 0$ for every value of x.

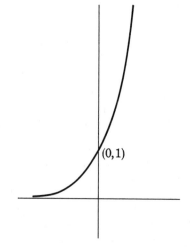

The fundamental property $L(ax) = L(a) + L(x)$ of the function $L(x)$ entails a similar basic result for the inverse function. Let us write b for $L(a)$, y for $L(x)$, and w for $L(ax)$, thus

$$b = L(a), \quad y = L(x),$$
$$w = L(ax), \quad w = b + y.$$

In terms of the inverse function we see that

FIG. 7.4   Sketch of $y = E(x)$ or $y = e^x$.

$$a = E(b), \quad x = E(y),$$
$$ax = E(w), \quad ax = E(b + y),$$

and hence

$$(11) \qquad E(b) \cdot E(y) = E(b + y).$$

This basic property of the E function is now used to analyze the function. If we set $y = 0$ we get $E(b) \cdot E(0) = E(b)$, and since $E(b)$ is positive whatever the value of b, we conclude that

$$(12) \qquad\qquad E(0) = 1.$$

If we set $b = 1$ and $y = 1$ in (11) we get $E(1) \cdot E(1) = E(2)$ or $E(2) = \{E(1)\}^2$. Then if we set $b = 2$ and $y = 1$ we get

$$E(3) = E(2) \cdot E(1), \quad \text{whence} \quad E(3) = \{E(1)\}^3.$$

Similarly, if we set $b = 3$ and $y = 1$ we get $E(4) = \{E(1)\}^4$, and a continuation of this process leads to

$$(13) \qquad\qquad E(n) = \{E(1)\}^n$$

for any positive integer n. For any positive rational number n/r let us form the product with r factors,

$$E(n/r)E(n/r)E(n/r) \dots E(n/r) = \{E(n/r)\}^r.$$

Applying (11) repeatedly we see that this product equals $E(n)$, and so from (13) we conclude that

$$(14) \qquad \{E(n/r)\}^r = E(n) = \{E(1)\}^n, \quad E(n/r) = \{E(1)\}^{n/r}.$$

Next, if we replace b by n/r and y by $-n/r$ in (11) we get, by use of (12) and (14),

$$(15) \qquad E(n/r)E(-n/r) = 1, \quad E(-n/r) = \{E(1)\}^{-n/r}.$$

It may be noted that $E(1)$ plays a central role in these equations, and so to simplify the notation we replace it by e. Thus (13), (14), and (15) can be written

$$E(n) = e^n, \quad E(n/r) = e^{n/r}, \quad E(-n/r) = e^{-n/r}.$$

Hence we can conclude that

$$(16) \qquad\qquad E(x) = e^x$$

for all rational values of x.

What about the irrational values of x? From our approach we know that $E(x)$ is defined and has meaning for irrational x, but how is e^x defined? Let us fix our ideas on one specific irrational number α, and let us say that

$$a_1, a_2, a_3 \dots$$

is a sequence of rational numbers having α as a limit. For example if α were $\sqrt{2}$ we could take the sequence to be

$$1, 1.4, 1.41, 1.414, 1.4142, \dots .$$

The natural thing to do is to define e^α as the limit of the sequence

(17) $$e^{a_1}, e^{a_2}, e^{a_3}, e^{a_4}, \dots .$$

But does this sequence have a limit? Our approach assures us that it does. For the sequence (17) can be written, because of (16), as

(18) $$E(a_1), E(a_2), E(a_3), E(a_4), \dots .$$

Furthermore, since the function $E(x)$ is differentiable, it is continuous by Theorem 1 of § 4.2, and consequently the limit of (18) exists and is equal to $E(\alpha)$. Hence the sequence (17) has the same limit, and we have proved that equation (16) holds for all values of x, rational and irrational.

This means that $E(x)$ is an exponential function e^x, where e is some constant. We will determine the precise value of e in the next section. For the moment we recall that e is $E(1)$, and so

$$E(1) = e, \quad L(e) = 1.$$

Now we proved that $L(2) < 1$ and $L(3) > 1$ in equation (9) of § 7.2, and since $L(x)$ is a monotonic increasing function, it follows that e lies between 2 and 3.

Furthermore since $E(x)$ is an exponential function, the inverse function must be a logarithmic function. Specifically, the inverse of the function

$$y = E(x) \quad \text{or} \quad y = e^x$$

can be written in either form.

$$x = L(y) \quad \text{or} \quad x = \log_e y.$$

Logarithms to base e are called natural logarithms, and throughout this book these logarithms are written without any base being shown. Thus $\log y$ means $\log_e y$. Logarithms to base 10 are called common logarithms, and we write such logarithms always with the base showing, e.g., $\log_{10} y$.

In view of all this we can rewrite Theorem 1 with $\log x$ in place of $L(x)$:

THEOREM 3. *If* $y = \log x$, *then* $dy/dx = 1/x$.

Also, the basic property in Theorem 2 can now be written in the form

(19) $$\log ax = \log a + \log x$$

for positive numbers a and x, and similarly (11) can be written in the form

(20) $$e^b \cdot e^y = e^{b+y}.$$

Next we state equation (10) as a theorem, with e^x in place of $E(x)$.

THEOREM 4. *If $y = e^x$, then $dy/dx = e^x$.*

The function e^x is monotonic, and its domain is the set of all real numbers, so the fundamental theorem of calculus gives the following result when applied to Theorem 4.

THEOREM 5. *For all real numbers a and b.*

$$\int_a^b e^x \, dx = e^b - e^a.$$

Just as Theorem 4 leads to Theorem 5, we can extend Theorem 3 in the same way, $\log x$ also being monotonic. However, the domain of the function $y = \log x$ is the set of positive real numbers, so some care must be taken with the limits of integration.

THEOREM 6. *If a and b are both positive or both negative, then*

$$\int_a^b \frac{dx}{x} = \log|b| - \log|a|.$$

PROOF. In case a and b are positive, then $|b| = b$ and $|a| = a$, so the result follows from Theorem 3 by an application of the fundamental theorem of calculus. In case a and b are negative, we use the fact that the graph of $y = 1/x$ is symmetric with respect to the origin in the following sense: To each point on the curve with positive coordinates, such as $(3, \frac{1}{3})$, there is a corresponding point with the same coordinates except for a change in sign, such as $(-3, -\frac{1}{3})$. Using the area interpretation of an integral as in § 3.4, we can see that for example

$$\int_{-9}^{-7} \frac{dx}{x} = - \int_7^9 \frac{dx}{x},$$

and in general

$$\int_a^b \frac{dx}{x} = - \int_{-b}^{-a} \frac{dx}{x}.$$

The integral on the right side of this equation can be evaluated because $-a$ and $-b$ are positive, and so we get

$$-\{\log(-a) - \log(-b)\} \quad \text{or} \quad \log|b| - \log|a|.$$

Thus the theorem is proved. Finally we note that the integral in

Theorem 6 has no meaning if a and b have opposite signs.

We now complete the proof of Theorem 7 of § 4.3 that the derivative of x^n is nx^{n-1}, for irrational n. For such values of n the meaning of x^n is obscure, so first we point out that the equation

$$x^n = e^{n\log x}$$

can serve as a definition of x^n for irrational n, because this formula does hold for rational values of n. To see this we observe that for $n = 1$ it follows from the fact that e^x and $\log x$, i.e. $E(x)$ and $L(x)$ are inverse functions. Then we can proceed by paralleling the steps used in equations (13) to (16) earlier in this section, with (20) now taking the place of (11). The steps are so similar that we omit details. Thus we define x^n to be $e^{n\log x}$ for irrational n. To differentiate x^n we take it in the form $e^{n\log x}$ and apply the chain rule, Theorem 11 of § 4.5, and Theorem 4 of this section to write

$$y = e^u, \quad u = n\log x, \quad y = e^{n\log x} = x^n,$$
$$\frac{dy}{dx} = \frac{dy}{du} \cdot \frac{du}{dx} = e^u \cdot n \cdot \frac{1}{x} = x^n \cdot n \cdot \frac{1}{x} = nx^{n-1}.$$

Finally, we use the derivative of the logarithm to get at the integral of $\tan x$. By combining Theorem 3 with the chain rule (Theorem 11 of § 4.5), we see that if $y = \log u$, where u is a differentiable function of x whose values are positive on an interval, then

$$\frac{dy}{dx} = \frac{1}{u} \cdot \frac{du}{dx} \quad \text{or} \quad \frac{d}{dx}(\log u) = \frac{1}{u} \cdot \frac{du}{dx}$$

on the interval. Taking u to be $\cos x$ we see that

$$\frac{dy}{dx} = \frac{d}{dx}[\log \cos x] = \frac{1}{\cos x} \cdot \frac{d}{dx}(\cos x) = \frac{1}{\cos x}(-\sin x) = -\tan x.$$

Applying the fundamental theorem of calculus we get

$$\int_a^b \tan x \, dx = \Big[-\log \cos x\Big]_a^b = -\log \cos b + \log \cos a$$

where we restrict a and b to the intervals, say, $-\pi/2 < a < \pi/2$, $-\pi/2 < b < \pi/2$, because the function $\tan x$ is not defined at $x = \pi/2$ and $x = -\pi/2$. Any real numbers a and b will do this in integration formula, provided only that $\tan x$ is defined on the closed interval from a to b, i.e., the interval including a and b.

Problems

1. Write $E(1)$, $E(2)$ and $E(3)$ in terms of e.
2. Evaluate $\log e$, $\log e^2$ and $\log e^3$.
3. Find the derivatives of

(a) $y = \log 2x$ (c) $y = \log(x+1)$

(b) $y = \log 4x$ (d) $y = \log(2x+1)$

4. Differentiate

$$y = \log\frac{x}{x+1}.$$

Suggestion: $\log a/b = \log a - \log b$.
5. Differentiate $y = \log x^3$.
6. Find the derivatives of

(a) $y = e^{x+1}$ (c) $y = xe^x$

(b) $y = e^{2x}$ (d) $y = e^{-x}$

7. Evaluate the integrals:

(a) $\displaystyle\int_0^1 e^x \, dx$ (c) $\displaystyle\int_{-e}^{-1} \frac{dx}{x}$

(b) $\displaystyle\int_3^9 \frac{dx}{x}$ (d) $\displaystyle\int_1^2 \frac{x+1}{x} \, dx$

8. For what real numbers x is $y = xe^{-x}$ a maximum or minimum?
9. For what positive value or values of x is $y = (1/x) + \log x$ a maximum or minimum?
*10. Prove that the areas bounded by the following two configurations are equal: (a) the curve $y = 1/x$ from $(\frac{1}{2}, 2)$ to $(2, \frac{1}{2})$ and the straight-line segments from $(2, \frac{1}{2})$ to $(2, 0)$, from $(2, 0)$ to $(\frac{1}{2}, 0)$, and from $(\frac{1}{2}, 0)$ to $(\frac{1}{2}, 2)$; (b) the curve $y = 1/x$ from $(1, 1)$ to $(4, \frac{1}{4})$ and the straight-line segments from $(4, \frac{1}{4})$ to $(4, 0)$, from $(4, 0)$ to $(1, 0)$, and from $(1, 0)$ to $(1, 1)$.
11. Prove that the tangent line to the curve $y = \log x$ at the point $(1, 0)$ crosses the x-axis at an angle of $45°$.
12. At what point on the curve $y = e_x$ does the tangent line have slope 1?
13. For all positive real numbers a and b, and all real numbers n except $n = -1$, prove that

$$\int_a^b x^n \, dx = \frac{b^{n+1} - a^{n+1}}{n+1}.$$

14. Differentiate $y = \log \sin x$, and use the result to prove that

$$\int_a^b \cot x \, dx = \log \sin b - \log \sin a,$$

for any real numbers a and b such that cot x is defined for all values of x from a to b inclusive, for example for a and b strictly between 0 and π.

15. Differentiate $y = \log(x+c)$, where c is a constant. Then evaluate the integral

$$\int_a^b \frac{dx}{x+c}$$

assuming that $a+c$ and $b+c$ are positive.

16. Differentiate $y = \log(x+k) - \log(x-k)$, where k is a constant, and use the result to prove that the indefinite integral

$$\int \frac{dx}{x^2 - k^2} = \frac{1}{2k} \log\left[\frac{x-k}{x+k}\right] + c,$$

provided $x+k$ and $x-k$ are positive.

17. Differentiate $y = xe^x - e^x$ and then evaluate

$$\int_0^1 xe^x \, dx$$

7.4 The Series Expansion for e^x. By a device very similar to the one used in § 6.2 to get expansions for sin x and cos x, we now derive an infinite series expansion for e^x. First we want to differentiate e^{-x}. We write

$$y = e^u, \quad u = -x,$$

and apply Theorem 11 of § 4.5. From Theorem 4 of the preceding section we get

$$\frac{dy}{du} = e^u, \quad \frac{du}{dx} = -1, \quad \frac{dy}{dx} = (e^u)(-1) = -e^{-x}, \quad \frac{d}{dx}(e^{-x}) = -e^{-x}.$$

Next we use the fundamental theorem of calculus (from § 5.3) to write

(21) $$\int_0^b e^{-x} \, dx = [-e^{-x}]_0^b = -e^{-b} + e^0 = 1 - e^{-b}.$$

For positive x we know that $e^x > 1$, so that by Theorem 6 of § 2.1,

$$e^{-x} = \frac{1}{e^x} < 1.$$

Thus for $x \geq 0$ we see that $e^{-x} \leq 1$. We now apply Theorem 8 of § 5.5 with $F(x)$ replaced by e^{-x}, $G(x)$ replaced by 1, $a = 0$ and b any positive number. We get, by use of (21),

$$\int_0^b e^{-x} \, dx \leq \int_0^b 1 \, dx, \quad 1 - e^{-b} \leq b, \quad 1 - b \leq e^{-b}.$$

This holds for any positive value of b, so $1-x \leqq e^{-x}$ holds for any positive x; it also holds for $x = 0$. Again we apply Theorem 8 of § 5.5, this time with $F(x)$ replaced by $1-x$ and $G(x)$ replaced by e^{-x}. We get

$$\int_0^b (1-x)\, dx \leqq \int_0^b e^{-x}\, dx, \quad b - \frac{b^2}{2} \leqq 1 - e^{-b}, \quad e^{-b} \leqq 1 - b + \frac{b^2}{2}.$$

This holds for any $b > 0$, so $e^{-x} \leqq 1 - x + x^2/2$ holds for any positive x; it also holds for $x = 0$. Once again we apply Theorem 8 of § 5.5, with $F(x)$ replaced by e^{-x} and $G(x)$ replaced by $1 - x + x^2/2$. We get

$$\int_0^b e^{-x}\, dx \leqq \int_0^b (1 - x + x^2/2)\, dx,$$

$$1 - e^{-b} \leqq b - \frac{b^2}{2} + \frac{b^3}{6} = \frac{b}{1!} - \frac{b^2}{2!} + \frac{b^3}{3!},$$

$$1 - \frac{b}{1!} + \frac{b^2}{2!} - \frac{b^3}{3!} \leqq e^{-b}.$$

Again we switch from b to x and apply Theorem 8 of § 5.5. Iteration of this process leads to the following chain of inequalities, valid for any non-negative x,

$$e^{-x} \leqq 1 \qquad\qquad e^{-x} \geqq 1 - \frac{x}{1!}$$

$$e^{-x} \leqq 1 - \frac{x}{1!} + \frac{x^2}{2!} \qquad e^{-x} \geqq 1 - \frac{x}{1!} + \frac{x^2}{2!} - \frac{x^3}{3!}$$

$$e^{-x} \leqq 1 - \frac{x}{1!} + \frac{x^2}{2!} - \frac{x^3}{3!} + \frac{x^4}{4!} \qquad e^{-x} \geqq 1 - \frac{x}{1!} + \frac{x^2}{2!} - \frac{x^3}{3!} + \frac{x^4}{4!} - \frac{x^5}{5!}$$

etc.

Thus for any non-negative x we see that e^{-x} is caught between successive partial sums of the series

$$(22) \qquad 1 - \frac{x}{1!} + \frac{x^2}{2!} - \frac{x^3}{3!} + \frac{x^4}{4!} - \frac{x^5}{5!} + \frac{x^6}{6!} - \frac{x^7}{7!} + \cdots.$$

Denoting the partial sums by $s_1, s_2, s_3, s_4, \ldots$ we have

$$s_1 = 1, \quad s_2 = 1 - \frac{x}{1!}, \quad s_3 = 1 - \frac{x}{1!} + \frac{x^2}{2!}, \quad s_4 = 1 - \frac{x}{1!} + \frac{x^2}{2!} - \frac{x^3}{3!}, \ldots.$$

Thus no member of the sequence

(23) $$s_1, s_3, s_5, s_7, \ldots$$

is less than e^{-x}, and on the other hand, no member of the sequence

(24) $$s_2, s_4, s_6, s_8, \ldots$$

is greater than e^{-x}.

Let us regard x as a fixed non-negative number for a moment, so that e^{-x} is fixed. We apply Theorem 14 of § 2.4, with e^{-x} playing the role of c, the sequence (23) in place of the sequence $\{a_n\}$, and the sequence (24) in place of the sequence $\{b_n\}$. In order to apply Theorem 14 of § 2.4, we must also know that $\lim(a_n - b_n) = 0$, in the notation of that theorem. In the present context the difference $a_n - b_n$ is $s_{2n-1} - s_{2n}$, and we see that

$$s_{2n-1} - s_{2n} = \frac{x^{2n-1}}{(2n-1)!}.$$

As n tends to infinity this tends to zero, by Theorems 2 and 3 of § 6.1. Thus all the hypotheses of Theorem 14 of § 2.4 are satisfied and we conclude that both sequences (23) and (24) have limit e^{-x}. But the sequences (23) and (24) are the partial sums of the sequence (22), and so we conclude that

(25) $$e^{-x} = 1 - \frac{x}{1!} + \frac{x^2}{2!} - \frac{x^3}{3!} + \frac{x^4}{4!} - \frac{x^5}{5!} + \frac{x^6}{6!} - \frac{x^7}{7!} + \ldots .$$

This expansion of e^{-x} into a series has been established only for non-negative values of x, that is, for all $x \geq 0$. If we replace x by $-x$ in (25) we get the more common form

(26) $$e^x = 1 + \frac{x}{1!} + \frac{x^2}{2!} + \frac{x^3}{3!} + \frac{x^4}{4!} + \frac{x^5}{5!} + \ldots .$$

Since (25) was proved for $x \geq 0$, we note that (26) has been established for $x \leq 0$, because x was switched to $-x$. Formula (26) is a very basic result which holds in fact for all values of x. To prove this, we must establish that (26) is correct for positive values of x, and this we now do.

We begin afresh with the function $f(x)$ defined by

$$f(x) = 1 + xe^c - e^x.$$

Here c is any fixed positive number, and the domain of the function is restricted to $0 \leq x \leq c$. Note that $f(0) = 0$ and that $f'(x) = e^c - e^x$.

We apply Theorem 15 of § 4.7. Since e^x is monotonic increasing, we see that $f'(x) > 0$ for $0 < x < c$. Hence $f(x)$ is monotonic increasing for $0 \leq x \leq c$, and it follows that

$$f(x) \geq 0, \quad 1 + xe^c - e^x \geq 0, \quad 1 \leq e^x \leq 1 + xe^c.$$

We apply Theorem 8 of § 5.5 to get

$$\int_0^b 1 \, dx \leq \int_0^b e^x \, dx \leq \int_0^b (1 + xe^c) \, dx$$

for any number b satisfying $0 \leq b \leq c$. Evaluating these integrals we have

$$b \leq e^b - 1 \leq b + \frac{b^2}{2} e^c.$$

Replacing b by x we see that

$$x \leq e^x - 1 \leq x + \frac{x^2}{2} e^c \quad \text{for} \quad 0 \leq x \leq c,$$

and we apply Theorem 8 of § 5.5 again to get

$$\int_0^b x \, dx \leq \int_0^b (e^x - 1) \, dx \leq \int_0^b \left(x + \frac{x^2}{2} e^c \right) dx,$$

$$\frac{b^2}{2} \leq e^b - 1 - b \leq \frac{b^2}{2} + \frac{b^3}{6} e^c \quad \text{for} \quad 0 \leq b \leq c.$$

Replacing b by x and applying Theorem 8 of § 5.5 again, we obtain

$$\int_0^b \frac{x^2}{2} dx \leq \int_0^b (e^x - 1 - x) \, dx \leq \int_0^b \left(\frac{x^2}{2} + \frac{x^3}{6} e^c \right) dx,$$

$$\frac{b^3}{6} \leq e^b - 1 - b - \frac{b^2}{2} \leq \frac{b^3}{6} + \frac{b^4}{24} e^c \quad \text{for} \quad 0 \leq b \leq c.$$

Repetition of this process leads to

$$\frac{b^n}{n!} \leq e^b - 1 - b - \frac{b^2}{2!} - \frac{b^3}{3!} - \cdots - \frac{b^{n-1}}{(n-1)!} \leq \frac{b^n}{n!} + \frac{b^{n+1}}{(n+1)!} e^c,$$

valid for any b satisfying $0 \leq b \leq c$. By Theorem 2 of § 6.1 we conclude that

$$\lim_{n \to \infty} \frac{b^n}{n!} = 0, \quad \lim_{n \to \infty} \left\{ \frac{b^n}{n!} + \frac{b^{n+1}}{(n+1)!} e^c \right\} = \lim \frac{b^n}{n!} + e^c \lim \frac{b^{n+1}}{(n+1)!}$$

$$= 0 + e^c \cdot 0 = 0.$$

Consequently, as n tends to infinity it follows from Theorem 17 of § 2.4 that

$$e^b - 1 - b - \frac{b^2}{2!} - \frac{b^3}{3!} - \ldots = 0.$$

Replacing b by x we obtain (26) for any x in the domain $0 \leq x \leq c$. But c is *any* positive number, and so (26) has been established for all positive values of x. Since (26) has already been proved for $x \leq 0$, we have now completely proved this formula for all values of x.

We are now in a position to compute the value of e, by setting $x = 1$ in (26). This gives

$$e = 1 + \frac{1}{1!} + \frac{1}{2!} + \frac{1}{3!} + \frac{1}{4!} + \frac{1}{5!} + \ldots ,$$

$$e = 2.71828 \ldots .$$

Problems

1. Check the arithmetic in the above computation of e to five decimal places.

2. Compute e^{-1} to four decimal places by use of formula (25).

3. Compute $e^{.1}$ to five decimal places.

4. At the opening of this section we found the derivative of $y = e^{-x}$. Verify the result by writing the function in the form $y = 1/e^x$, and using Theorem 6 of § 4.3.

5. Presuming that it is correct to differentiate an infinite series term by term (as it is under certain conditions), differentiate (26) term by term and verify Theorem 4 of § 7.3.

6. Compute the value of $\sqrt{e}$ to three decimal places by substituting the appropriate value of x in (26). Verify your answer by taking the square root of 2.71828.

7. Presuming that it is correct to multiply two infinite series term by term, multiply equations (25) and (26), computing all powers up to x^5 in the product.

8. With the same presumption as in the preceding problem, multiply the series for e^x in (26) by itself as far as terms in x^5. Check that the same result can be obtained by replacing x by $2x$ in (26).

*9. What function $f(x)$ has the properties $f'(x) = f(x)$ and $f(0) = 4$?

*10. What function $g(x)$ has the properties $g'(x) = -g(x)$ and $g(1) = 1$?

7.5 The Number e. We now develop a well-known expression for e as a limit, namely formula (27) below. We start with Theorem 3 of § 7.3, which can be written in the form

$$\lim_{\Delta x \to 0} \frac{\log(x + \Delta x) - \log x}{\Delta x} = \frac{1}{x}.$$

Taking $x = 1$, and using $\log 1 = 0$, we get

$$\lim_{\Delta x \to 0} \left[\frac{1}{\Delta x} \log(1 + \Delta x) \right] = 1.$$

We let Δx tend to zero through the positive values $1, \frac{1}{2}, \frac{1}{3}, \frac{1}{4}, \ldots$ so that the above limit becomes the limit of a sequence. Writing $1/n$ for Δx, we see that $\Delta x \to 0$ implies $n \to \infty$, and so we have

$$\lim_{n \to \infty} \left[n \log \left(1 + \frac{1}{n} \right) \right] = 1.$$

To the left member of this equation we apply equation (8) of § 7.2 to write $n \, \log(1 + 1/n)$ in the form $\log(1 + 1/n)^n$, and thus we get

$$\lim_{n \to \infty} \log(1 + 1/n)^n = 1.$$

For convenience at this point, let us write a_n for $\log(1 + 1/n)^n$, so that we have a sequence $a_1, a_2, a_3, a_4, \ldots$ with limit 1.

Now as we noted in our discussion following (18) in § 7.3, the function $E(x)$ or e^x is continuous because it is differentiable. Consequently, by the definition of a continuous function given in § 2.9, we conclude that the sequence

$$e^{a_1}, e^{a_2}, e^{a_3}, e^{a_4}, \ldots, e^{a_n}, \ldots$$

has limit e^1, or e. But since $E(x)$ and $L(x)$ are inverse functions, we see that

$$e^{a_n} = E(a_n) = E(\log(1 + 1/n)^n) = E(L(1 + 1/n)^n) = (1 + 1/n)^n,$$

and

$$(27) \qquad\qquad e = \lim_{n \to \infty} (1 + 1/n)^n.$$

Some calculus books establish the properties of e, e^x, and $\log x$ by using equation (27) as a definition of e. In our approach, (27) is a property of e, and we now use this equation to show an interesting interpretation of this basic mathematical constant. If one dollar could be invested at 100 per cent rate of interest for 1 year, it would accumulate to $1 + 1$ dollars at the end of the year. If the rate were 100 per cent compounded semi-annually, the amount accumulated would be $1 + \frac{1}{2}$ dollars at the end of six months, and so

$$(1 + \tfrac{1}{2}) + \tfrac{1}{2}(1 + \tfrac{1}{2}) = (1 + \tfrac{1}{2})(1 + \tfrac{1}{2}) = (1 + \tfrac{1}{2})^2$$

dollars at the end of the year. If the interest rate were 100 per cent compounded three times during the year, the effect would be to multiply by a factor of $1+\frac{1}{3}$ at the end of each interest period, $1+\frac{1}{3}$ because we need a factor 1 to give the original amount and a factor $\frac{1}{3}$ to account for the interest. Hence the accumulated amount at the end of the year would be

$$(1+\tfrac{1}{3})^3$$

dollars. Similarly, quarterly additions of compound interest would yield, by repeated multiplication by $1+\frac{1}{4}$, a total of

$$(1+\tfrac{1}{4})^4$$

dollars at the end of the year. In general, if the interest rate is 100 per cent compounded n times a year, one dollar would increase to

$$(1+1/n)^n$$

dollars at the end of the year. But by (27) the limit of this expression as n tends to infinity is e, and so e can be interpreted as the accumulated amount at the end of one year when one dollar earns interest at the rate of 100 per cent compounded continuously. Since ordinary compound interest represents growth in spurts, we see that e is related to a steady, continuous growth. And so is e^x; for example if instead of using an interest rate of 100 per cent compounded continuously we had used a rate of $(100x)$ per cent, then the continuous compounding of interest would have increased the principal of one dollar to an amount of e^x dollars. In other words, we analyzed the special case with $x = 1$. Because of such properties as these, the graphs of the function $y = e^x$ and of similar exponential equations are called the growth curves.

Problems

1. Compute $(1+\frac{1}{2})^2$, $(1+\frac{1}{3})^3$ and $(1+\frac{1}{4})^4$ to two decimal places.
2. Evaluate the limits

(a) $\displaystyle\lim_{n\to\infty}\left(1+\frac{1}{2n}\right)^{2n}$
    (c) $\displaystyle\lim_{n\to\infty}\left(1+\frac{1}{n^2}\right)^{n2}$

(b) $\displaystyle\lim_{n\to\infty}\left(1+\frac{1}{2n+1}\right)^{2n+1}$
    (d) $\displaystyle\lim_{n\to\infty}\left(1+\frac{1}{3n}\right)^{3n}$

Suggestion: Use Theorem 3 of § 6.1.

*3. Evaluate the limits

(a) $\displaystyle\lim_{n\to\infty}\left(1+\frac{1}{n}\right)^{n+1}$
    (b) $\displaystyle\lim_{n\to\infty}\left(1+\frac{1}{n}\right)^{2n}$

(c) $\displaystyle\lim_{n\to\infty}\left(1+\frac{1}{2n}\right)^n$ (e) $\displaystyle\lim_{n\to\infty}\left(1+\frac{1}{3n}\right)^n$

(d) $\displaystyle\lim_{n\to\infty}\left(1+\frac{1}{n}\right)^{3n}$ (f) $\displaystyle\lim_{n\to\infty}\left(1+\frac{1}{2n}\right)^{2n+1}$

Suggestion: Use Theorem 12 of § 2.4.

4. If \$100.00 is invested at 5% per annum, it accumulates to \$105.00 at the end of one year. Compute the amount that would be accumulated at the end of one year if the interest (at 5%) were compounded continuously.

7.6 The Series Expansion for the Logarithmic Function.

Although the reader is probably familiar with the concept of a geometric progression and its sum, nevertheless we develop the basic idea here because it is quite essential to our method. Consider the sum

$$S = 1+r+r^2+r^3+ \ \dots \ +r^{n-2}+r^{n-1},$$

where n is some positive integer. To find an algebraic formula for this sum, we multiply the above equation by r to get

$$rS = r+r^2+r^3+r^4+ \ \dots \ r^{n-1}+r^n.$$

Subtracting these two equations we get

$$S-rS = 1-r^n, \quad \text{or} \quad S(1-r) = 1-r^n,$$

since most of the terms on the right sides cancel. Dividing by $1-r$ we get $S = (1-r^n)/(1-r)$, and so

$$(28) \qquad 1+r+r^2+r^3+ \ \dots \ +r^{n-2}+r^{n-1} = \frac{1-r^n}{1-r} = \frac{1}{1-r} - \frac{r^n}{1-r}.$$

This equation is not valid in case $r = 1$, because in this case $1-r = 0$ and the division is impossible. But (28) holds for any number r except $r = 1$, and for any natural number n. So also the following variation on (28) holds for $x \neq 1$,

$$(29) \qquad \frac{1}{1-x} = 1+x+x^2+x^3+\dots+x^{n-2}+x^{n-1}+\frac{x^n}{1-x}.$$

We plan to integrate this equation. To begin, we want to find the integral of $1/(1-x)$. Theorem 3 of § 7.3 suggests that we should look at the derivative of $y = \log(1-x)$. Using this theorem, and also Theorem 11 of § 4.5, we can write

$$y = \log u, \quad u = 1-x, \quad \frac{dy}{du} = \frac{1}{u}, \quad \frac{du}{dx} = -1,$$

$$\frac{dy}{dx} = \frac{dy}{du} \cdot \frac{du}{dx} = -\frac{1}{u} = \frac{-1}{1-x},$$

(30)
$$\frac{d}{dx}\{\log(1-x)\} = \frac{-1}{1-x}.$$

With this background, we integrate (29) to get

(31)
$$\int_0^b \frac{dx}{1-x} = \int_0^b 1\,dx + \int_0^b x\,dx + \int_0^b x^2\,dx + \int_0^b x^3\,dx$$
$$+ \dots + \int_0^b x^{n-2}\,dx + \int_0^b x^{n-1}\,dx + \int_0^b \frac{x^n}{1-x}\,dx.$$

In view of (30) we see that

$$\int_0^b \frac{dx}{1-x} = [-\log(1-x)]_0^b = -\log(1-b) + \log 1 = -\log(1-b),$$

and so (31) can be written as

(32) $$-\log(1-b) = b + \frac{b^2}{2} + \frac{b^3}{3} + \frac{b^4}{4} + \dots + \frac{b^{n-1}}{n-1} + \frac{b^n}{n} + \int_0^b \frac{x^n}{1-x}\,dx.$$

This last integral will not be evaluated, but we will establish that it tends to zero as n tends to infinity, provided that b is suitably restricted. For convenience we write

(33)
$$I_n = \int_0^b \frac{x^n}{1-x}\,dx.$$

Now the fact is that $I_n \to 0$ as $n \to \infty$ for all values of b satisfying $-1 \le b < 1$; but we shall prove this only for the values satisfying $0 \le b < 1$, since this is all that we shall need for our purposes. We apply Theorem 9 of § 5.5. With b satisfying $0 \le b < 1$ we notice that the values of x involved in the integral (33) satisfy

$$0 \le x \le b, \quad x^n \le b^n, \quad 1-x \ge 1-b,$$
$$\frac{1}{1-x} \le \frac{1}{1-b}, \quad \frac{x^n}{1-x} \le \frac{b^n}{1-b}.$$

Hence we can take the M of Theorem 9 of § 5.5 to be $b^n/(1-b)$, and so we conclude that

$$I_n = \int_0^b \frac{x^n}{1-x}\,dx \le \frac{b^n}{1-b}(b-0) = \frac{b^{n+1}}{1-b}.$$

Also we observe that $I_n \geqq 0$, since the integrand is non-negative for the values of b under consideration. Thus we can write

$$(34) \qquad\qquad 0 \leqq I_n \leqq \frac{b^{n+1}}{1-b}.$$

Now $\lim b^n = 0$ as n tends to infinity, by Theorem 1 of § 6.1, and so

$$\lim_{n \to \infty} \frac{b^{n+1}}{1-b} = \lim_{n \to \infty} b^n \cdot \lim_{n \to \infty} \frac{b}{1-b} = 0 \cdot \frac{b}{1-b} = 0.$$

Hence $\lim I_n = 0$ by Theorem 9 of § 2.3. It follows that if we let n tend to infinity in (32) we get

$$-\log(1-b) = b + \frac{b^2}{2} + \frac{b^3}{3} + \frac{b^4}{4} + \frac{b^5}{5} + \dots \; .$$

This holds for b restricted to $0 \leqq b < 1$, and so we have the infinite series for $\log(1-b)$,

$$(35) \qquad \log(1-b) = -b - \frac{b^2}{2} - \frac{b^3}{3} - \frac{b^4}{4} - \frac{b^5}{5} - \dots \; .$$

A more thorough analysis of equations (32) and (33) can be given to show that (35) is valid for values of b satisfying $-1 \leqq b < 1$, but we will not go into that.

Problems

1. Compute log .9 to four decimal places. Suggestion: Set $b = .1$ in (35).
2. Compute log. 99 to four decimal places.
3. What does (35) give us if we set $b = 0$?

7.7 The Computation of Logarithms. Equation (35) can be used to compute logarithms. For example if we want to find the value of log 2, we take $b = \frac{1}{2}$ in (35), and use the fact that $\log \frac{1}{2} = -\log 2$ to get

$$\log\frac{1}{2} = -\log 2 = -\frac{1}{2} - \frac{1}{2}\left(\frac{1}{2}\right)^2 - \frac{1}{3}\left(\frac{1}{2}\right)^3 - \frac{1}{4}\left(\frac{1}{2}\right)^4 - \dots \; .$$

The value of log 2 to four decimal places is .6931. In the same way we could take $b = \frac{2}{3}$ in (35) to obtain the approximate decimal value of log 3. But it would be better to take $b = \frac{1}{3}$, because the smaller the value of b, the more rapidly does the series (35) converge, i.e., the more rapidly does it tend to its limit. With $b = \frac{1}{3}$ we would get log $\frac{2}{3}$, and this could be subtracted from log 2 to give log 3:

$$\log 2 - \log \tfrac{2}{3} = \log.$$

But we drop this approach, and now show another way of getting at log 3 by using series that converge even more rapidly. First we use $b = \tfrac{1}{5}$ and $b = \tfrac{1}{10}$ in (35), thus

$$\log\frac{4}{5} = -\frac{1}{5} - \frac{1}{2}\left(\frac{1}{5}\right)^2 - \frac{1}{3}\left(\frac{1}{5}\right)^3 - \frac{1}{4}\left(\frac{1}{5}\right)^4 - \ldots \cong -.2231,$$

$$\log\frac{9}{10} = -\frac{1}{10} - \frac{1}{2}\left(\frac{1}{10}\right)^2 - \frac{1}{3}\left(\frac{1}{10}\right)^3 - \frac{1}{4}\left(\frac{1}{10}\right)^4 - \ldots \cong -.1054,$$

where the symbol $\cong$ stands for "is approximately equal to". Then we can write

$$\log 5 = 2\log 2 - \log 4/5 \cong 2(.6931) + .2231 = 1.6093,$$
$$\log 10 = \log 2 + \log 5 \cong .6931 + 1.6094 = 2.3024.$$

At this stage we have picked up an error in the last decimal place, which is to be expected because the errors in the approximations are piling up as we combine our results. The value of log 10 to four decimal places is 2.3026, and that of log 5 is 1.6094. Finally we have

$$\log 9 = \log 10 + \log(9/10) \cong 2.2036 - .1054 = 2.1972,$$
$$\log 3 = \tfrac{1}{2}\log 9 \cong 1.0986.$$

All these are natural logarithms, that is, logarithms to base e. To compute logarithms to base 10, common logarithms as they are called, we use the identity

(36) $$\log_{10}a = \log_e a \cdot \log_{10}e \text{ for } a > 0.$$

To prove this, let us write α, β, and γ for these three logarithms, that is

$$\alpha = \log_{10}a, \quad \beta = \log_e a, \quad \gamma = \log_{10}e.$$

Then we can establish (36) by observing that

$$a = 10^\alpha, \quad a = e^\beta, \quad e = 10^\gamma, \quad a = (10^\gamma)^\beta = 10^{\gamma\beta}, \quad 10^\alpha = 10^{\gamma\beta},$$
$$\alpha = \gamma\beta.$$

In order to use (36) we need the value of $\log_{10}e$, and we can get this by setting $a = 10$:

$$\log_{10}10 = 1 = \log_e 10 \cdot \log_{10}e.$$

We have already established that $\log_e 10 \cong 2.3026$, and so we find that

$$\log_{10} e = \frac{1}{\log_e 10} \cong \frac{1}{2.3026} \cong .4343.$$

Substituting this in (36) we get

$$\log_{10} a \cong .4343 \log_e a.$$

To compute $\log_{10} 2$, for example, we use the previously computed log 2 $\cong .6931$ to get

$$\log_{10} 2 \cong (.4343)(.6931) \cong .3010.$$

Problems

1. Compute the following to four decimal places.
   - (a) $\log_{10} 3$
   - (b) $\log_{10} 5$
   - (c) $\log_{10} 6$
   - (d) $\log_{10} 1.6$
2. Compute the following to four decimal places.
   - (a) $\log 7$
   - (b) $\log_{10} 7$
   - (c) $\log 11$
   - (d) $\log_{10} 11$
3. Let a, b, c be positive numbers, with $a \neq 1$, $b \neq 1$, and $c \neq 1$. Prove that

$$\log_b a \, \log_c b \, \log_a c = 1.$$

Suggestion: Use an argument similar to the proof of (36), say by writing u, v, and w for the three logarithms so that $b^u = a$, $c^v = b$, and $a^w = c$. Substitute the value of c in the last of these three equations into the second one to get $a^{wv} = b$. Then substitute this value of b into $b^u = a$.

4. With a and b as in the preceding question, prove that

$$\log_b a \, \log_a b = 1$$

by replacing c by a.

5. Prove that

$$\log_b a = \frac{\log_c a}{\log_c b}.$$

6. Compute $\log_2 5$ to two decimal places. Suggestion: Set $c = e$ in the preceding question.

7. Compute $\log_3 2$ to three decimal places.

7.8 Summary of Formulas.

$$\frac{d}{dx}(\log x) = \frac{1}{x} \qquad \frac{d}{dx}(\log u) = \frac{1}{u} \cdot \frac{du}{dx}$$

(natural logarithms throughout)

$$\int_a^b \frac{dx}{x} = \log|b| - \log|a|,$$

with a and b both positive or both negative.

$$\frac{d}{dx}(e^x) = e^x \qquad \int_a^b e^x \, dx = e^b - e^a$$

$$\int_a^b \tan x \, dx = \log \cos a - \log \cos b,$$

with a and b strictly between $-\dfrac{\pi}{2}$ and $\dfrac{\pi}{2}$, for example.

$$\int_a^b \cot x \, dx = \log \sin b - \log \sin a,$$

with a and b strictly between 0 and π, for example.

$$\int_a^b x^n \, dx = \frac{b^{n+1} - a^{n+1}}{n+1}$$

for all real numbers a, b, n with $n \neq -1$.

$$e = \lim_{n \to \infty} \left(1 + \frac{1}{n}\right)^n = 1 + \frac{1}{1!} + \frac{1}{2!} + \frac{1}{3!} + \frac{1}{4!} \cdots$$

$$e^x = 1 + x + \frac{x^2}{2!} + \frac{x^3}{3!} + \frac{x^4}{4!} + \cdots$$

$$\log(1-x) = -x - \frac{x^2}{2} - \frac{x^3}{3} - \frac{x^4}{4} - \frac{x^5}{5} - \cdots,$$

if x satisfies $-1 \leq x < 1$.

CHAPTER 8

FURTHER APPLICATIONS

8.0. This chapter, containing some additional applications of calculus, differs from the earlier chapters in that there is no sequential development of the material. The sections can be read independently, and therefore in any order, except for these restrictions: §§ 8.1 and 8.2 constitute a unit, an item of theory followed by an application; the mixing problem in § 8.5 leads to essentially the same equation as in § 8.4, and so one step of the argument is carried over intact.

8.1 The Series Expansion for the Arc Tangent Function. We can get an infinite series for arc tan x by using a scheme quite similar to that for $\log(1-b)$ in § 7.6. We replace r by $-x^2$ in equation (28) of § 7.6 to get, after switching terms around,

$$(1) \qquad \frac{1}{1+x^2} = 1 - x^2 + x^4 - x^6 + x^8 - \ldots + (-1)^{n-2}x^{2n-4}$$

$$+ (-1)^{n-1}x^{2n-2} + (-1)^n \frac{x^{2n}}{1+x^2}.$$

Since (28) was an identity, valid for all values of r except $r = 1$, we see that this equation (1) holds for all real values of x without exception. This is so because $-x^2 = 1$ has no solution in real numbers; and we have no concern with complex numbers in our analysis.

In order to integrate equation (1), we first use Theorem 13 of § 4.6 to get

$$\int_0^b \frac{dx}{1+x^2} = [\text{arc tan } x]_0^b = \text{arc tan } b - \text{arc tan } 0 = \text{arc tan } b.$$

171

Then if we integrate equation (1) term by term, with limits 0 to b on the integration, we get

$$(2) \qquad \arctan b = b - \frac{b^3}{3} + \frac{b^5}{5} - \frac{b^7}{7} + \frac{b^9}{9} - \cdots$$

$$+ (-1)^{n-2} \frac{b^{2n-3}}{2n-3} + (-1)^{n-1} \frac{b^{2n-1}}{2n-1} + (-1)^n \int_0^b \frac{x^{2n}}{1+x^2} \, dx.$$

We show that the last term tends to zero as n tends to infinity if b satisfies $0 \leq b \leq 1$. Since $x^2 \geq 0$ for every value of x, it follows that

$$1 + x^2 \geq 1, \quad \frac{1}{1+x^2} \leq 1, \quad \frac{x^{2n}}{1+x^2} \leq x^{2n}.$$

We apply Theorem 8 of § 5.5 with $F(x)$ and $G(x)$ replaced by $x^n/(1+x^2)$ and x^n respectively, to get

$$(3) \qquad \int_0^b \frac{x^{2n}}{1+x^2} \, dx \leq \int_0^b x^{2n} \, dx = \left[\frac{x^{2n+1}}{2n+1} \right]_0^b = \frac{b^{2n+1}}{2n+1}.$$

Since we are restricting b to the interval $0 \leq b \leq 1$ we see that

$$0 \leq b^{2n+1} \leq 1, \quad \lim_{n \to \infty} \frac{b^{2n+1}}{2n+1} = \lim b^{2n+1} \cdot \lim \frac{1}{2n+1} = 0.$$

It follows from (3) that the limit of the integral is also zero as $n \to \infty$, by the usual application of Theorem 9 of § 2.3. Thus equation (2) becomes, as $n \to \infty$

$$(4) \qquad \arctan b = b - \frac{b^3}{3} + \frac{b^5}{5} - \frac{b^7}{7} + \frac{b^9}{9} - \frac{b^{11}}{11} + \cdots.$$

What is the range of validity of equation (4)? In developing the equation we restricted b to the interval $0 \leq b \leq 1$. However, since $\arctan(-b) = -\arctan b$, as illustrated in Figure 4.10 of § 4.6, and since all the terms on the right side of (4) also change sign when b is replaced by $-b$, we see that (4) is valid for b in the interval $-1 \leq b \leq 1$.

8.2 The Computation of π. Equation (4) of the preceding section enables us to compute the value of π. If we take $b = 1$, and recall that $\arctan 1 = \pi/4$, we get

$$\frac{\pi}{4} = 1 - \frac{1}{3} + \frac{1}{5} - \frac{1}{7} + \frac{1}{9} - \frac{1}{11} + \cdots.$$

This equation, elegant though it is, does not lend itself to computation because the series converges very slowly, so that a considerable calculation is necessary for accuracy to, say, four or five decimal places.

A better equation for computational purposes can be had by taking $b = \sqrt{3}/3$ in (4). From elementary geometry we know that

$$\tan\frac{\pi}{6} = \frac{\sqrt{3}}{3}, \quad \text{arc}\tan\frac{\sqrt{3}}{3} = \frac{\pi}{6},$$

and so

$$\frac{\pi}{6} = \frac{\sqrt{3}}{3} - \frac{1}{3}\left(\frac{\sqrt{3}}{3}\right)^3 + \frac{1}{5}\left(\frac{\sqrt{3}}{3}\right)^5 - \frac{1}{7}\left(\frac{\sqrt{3}}{3}\right)^7 + \dots.$$

Multiplying by 6 and simplifying we have

$$(5) \quad \pi = 2\sqrt{3}\left[1 - \frac{1}{3.3} + \frac{1}{5.3^2} - \frac{1}{7.3^3} + \frac{1}{9.3^4} - \frac{1}{11.3^5} + \dots\right].$$

Yet another equation for π can be arrived at by using the trigonometric identity

$$(6) \quad \tan(\alpha+\beta) = \frac{\tan\alpha + \tan\beta}{1 - \tan\alpha\tan\beta}.$$

If we take $\alpha = \text{arc}\tan\frac{1}{2}$ and $\beta = \text{arc}\tan\frac{1}{3}$ we get

$$\tan(\alpha+\beta) = \frac{\frac{1}{2} + \frac{1}{3}}{1 - \frac{1}{2}\cdot\frac{1}{3}} = 1, \quad \text{and so} \quad \alpha+\beta = \frac{\pi}{4}.$$

This leads to the following relation, by use of equation (4),

$$(7) \quad \frac{\pi}{4} = \text{arc}\tan\frac{1}{2} + \text{arc}\tan\frac{1}{3}$$

$$= \left[\frac{1}{2} - \frac{1}{3.2^3} + \frac{1}{5.2^5} - \frac{1}{7.2^7} + \dots\right]$$

$$+ \left[\frac{1}{3} - \frac{1}{3.3^3} + \frac{1}{5.3^5} - \frac{1}{7.3^7} + \dots\right].$$

The value of π can be computed to as many decimal places as we please by use of equation (5) or equation (7).

Problems

1. Use (5) to compute the value of π to four decimal places.
2. Use (7) to compute the value of π to four decimal places.
3. Compute arc tan .1 to four decimal places.

4. Compute arc tan 10 to four decimal places. Suggestion: Equation (4) cannot be used with $b = 10$. Prove that arc tan $10 +$ arc tan $.1 = \pi/2$.

5. Compute arc tan 2 to four decimal places.

6. Verify that the error in using $22/7$ as an approximation to π is slightly larger than $.0012$.

8.3 The Velocity of Escape. Consider the following problem. At what initial velocity need an object be shot upwards from the surface of the earth in order to escape, so that it does not fall back to the surface of the earth? To attack this question, let us begin by stating what the conditions of the problem are. We shall disregard the resistance caused by the atmosphere at the surface of the earth. We shall presume that the initial thrust applied to the object is not directed vertically, but in the appropriate direction to counteract the earth's rotation. Thus the object is presumed to move in a straight line pointing directly away from the earth, so that if this line were continued backwards it would pass through the center of the earth. Furthermore the problem is idealized in the sense that the entire universe consists only of the earth and the object. Thus we are dealing with a simple case of a two body problem; the complications that arise with more than two bodies are considerable. Finally we shall presume that after the initial thrust there is no further force applied to the object except the gravitational pull of the earth.

In solving the problem we shall use the inverse square law of gravitation. The precise meaning of this will be formulated at the point in the discussion where it is used.

	P	Q
	x	$x+\Delta x$
	t	$t+\Delta t$
	v	$v+\Delta v$

FIG. 8.1

Consider the object at a time t (in seconds) after the initial thrust, so that it left the surface of the earth at time $t = 0$. Suppose that at time t the object has reached a point P, as in Figure 8.1, at a distance x miles from the center of the earth. Since we are measuring distance from the center of the earth, we note that $x = 4000$ when $t = 0$, taking the radius of the earth as 4000 miles. Next consider the object as it passes a point Q a little farther away from the earth. Suppose that the elapsed time is now $t + \Delta t$ and that Q is at a distance $x + \Delta x$ from the center of the earth. Since the object is moving away from the earth, the changes Δx in the x coordinate and Δt in the t coordinate are positive quantities.

Now in moving from P to Q the object has traversed a distance Δx in time Δt, and so its average velocity in this motion is $\Delta x/\Delta t$. We are using here the basic idea that velocity is distance divided by time. If we let Δt tend to zero we get the velocity v of the object as it passes the point P, thus

$$(8) \qquad v = \lim_{\Delta t \to 0} \frac{\Delta x}{\Delta t}.$$

This equation is the definition of velocity at a point, and it should be noted that the limit concept is central to this definition.

Now if v denotes the velocity of the object as it passes the point P, it is natural to let $v + \Delta v$ denote the velocity of the object as it passes Q. Because the flight of the object is being retarded by the gravitational pull of the earth, that is to say, the object is slowing down as it moves from P to Q, it follows that Δv is negative. Just as velocity is the ratio of distance to time, so acceleration is the ratio of velocity to time. Thus the average acceleration of the object as it moves from P to Q is $\Delta v / \Delta t$, and so the acceleration a at the point P is

$$(9) \qquad a = \lim_{\Delta t \to 0} \frac{\Delta v}{\Delta t}.$$

Since Δv is negative, so is a.

We are now in a position to say what is meant by our basic assumption of the inverse square law: the force exerted on the object by the gravitational pull of the earth is inversely proportional to the square of the distance from the center of the earth to the object. Further, since acceleration is directly proportional to the force exerted (this is Newton's second law of motion, which the reader may have met in its mathematical form, $F = ma$), we conclude that the acceleration is inversely proportional to the square of the distance,

$$(10) \qquad a = -\frac{k}{x^2}.$$

The symbol k is the constant of proportionality. Why do we write a minus sign in equation (10)? For this reason, that a is negative in our problem, and so if we want a positive constant of proportionality k, we must include a minus sign. If we had omitted the minus sign in (10), then k would be negative, which would have been less convenient although not incorrect.

The constant of proportionality k can be determined from standard experimental data. At the surface of the earth the acceleration due to gravity has the value $-.00609$, the units of distance and time being miles and seconds. (This is more commonly given as -32.16, in units of feet and seconds.) Taking the radius of the earth as 4000 miles, we get from (10)

(11) $$-.00609 = -\frac{k}{(4000)^2}, \quad k = 9.74 \times 10^4.$$

Next if we write (8) in the reciprocal form $1/v = \lim(\Delta t/\Delta x)$, and if we multiply this by (9), we get

$$\frac{a}{v} = \lim \frac{\Delta v}{\Delta t} \cdot \lim \frac{\Delta t}{\Delta x} = \lim \frac{\Delta v}{\Delta t} \cdot \frac{\Delta t}{\Delta x} = \lim \frac{\Delta v}{\Delta x} = \frac{dv}{dx},$$

where these limits are taken as Δt, and so also Δx, tend to zero. Also we replace a by its value from (10) to get

(12) $$\frac{dv}{dx} = \frac{a}{v} = -\frac{k}{vx^2}, \quad 2v\frac{dv}{dx} = -2kx^{-2},$$

where we have multiplied by $2v$ for a special reason. Defining V as the square of the velocity, $V = v^2$, we see by the chain rule of § 4.5 that

$$\frac{dV}{dx} = \frac{dV}{dv} \cdot \frac{dv}{dx} = 2v\frac{dv}{dx},$$

so that (12) can be written as

(13) $$\frac{dV}{dx} = -2kx^{-2}.$$

This says that there is a certain function V whose derivative is $-2kx^{-2}$. But $2kx^{-1}$ has this same derivative, by Theorem 7 of § 4.3. When two functions, V and $2kx^{-1}$, have the same derivative, what can we conclude? By Theorem 7 of § 5.4 we can conclude that these functions differ by a constant,

$$V = 2kx^{-1} + c, \quad v^2 = \frac{2k}{x} + c,$$

(14) $$v^2 = \frac{1.95 \times 10^5}{x} + c.$$

By interpreting equation (14) we now solve the problem posed at the beginning of this section. Equation (14) gives the velocity v of the object as a function of the distance x from the center of the earth, but in terms of a constant c which has not been determined. Let us try a numerical example to see how c can be evaluated. Suppose that an object is hurled into space with an initial velocity of 10 miles per second, just to take a number at random. Then in equation (14) we have $v = 10$ when $x = 4000$; thus

$$100 = \frac{1.95 \times 10^5}{4000} + c = 48.7 + c, \quad c = 51.3.$$

Thus c is determined when we specify an initial velocity for the object. Notice that in this case of an initial velocity of 10 miles per second, equation (14) can be rewritten as

$$v^2 = \frac{1.95 \times 10^5}{x} + 51.3.$$

From this equation we see that as x increases v decreases, as is to be expected. But v never becomes zero no matter how large we take x to be, because of the presence of the positive constant 51.3. As x gets indefinitely large, v^2 tends to 51.3.

On the other hand let us see what happens in equation (14) if we presume an initial velocity of 9 miles per second for the object. In this case (14) gives us

$$81 = \frac{1.95 \times 10^5}{4000} + c = 48.7 + c, \quad c = 32.3,$$

and so for initial velocity 9 equation (14) becomes

$$v^2 = \frac{1.95 \times 10^5}{x} + 32.3.$$

As x gets indefinitely large, v^2 tends to 32.3.

Thus we conclude that while 9 miles per second is enough of an initial velocity to get and keep the object away from the earth, it is more than enough because the object will have a velocity of at least $\sqrt{32.3}$ no matter how large x is. Hence the smallest possible initial velocity is the one that yields $c = 0$ in (14), and so we write

$$v^2 = \frac{1.95 \times 10^5}{x}.$$

Another way of establishing that $c = 0$ for the smallest possible initial velocity that permits escape is to observe that the velocity v

should tend to zero as x tends to infinity, and so from (14) we get

$$\lim_{x\to\infty} v^2 = \lim_{x\to\infty}\left[\frac{1.95\times 10^5}{x}+c\right] = 0,$$

$$\lim\left[\frac{1.95\times 10^5}{x}\right]+\lim[c] = 0+c = 0.$$

In any event we have (14) with $c = 0$, and we determine the initial velocity by setting $x = 4000$ to get

$$v^2 = \frac{1.95\times 10^5}{4000}, \quad v = 6.98.$$

Thus we have established that the minimum velocity of escape is 6.98 miles per second.

Problems

*1. Let g denote the acceleration of gravity at the surface of any planet. Assuming the planet to be a sphere of radius r, prove that the velocity of escape equals $\sqrt{2gr}$.

*2. Given the following table of approximate values,

	RADIUS IN MILES	MEAN DENSITY (WATER = 1)
EARTH	4000	5.5
MOON	1100	3.3
MARS	2100	4.0

prove that $g_2/g_1 = .165$ and $g_3/g_1 = .38$, where g_1, g_2, g_3 are the accelerations of gravity on the Earth, the moon, and Mars. Suggestion: Newton's law of gravitation implies that g is directly proportional to the mass of the planet, and inversely proportional to the square of the radius.

*3. Use all preceding data to show that the velocities of escape from the moon and Mars are approximately 1.5 and 3.1 miles per second.

8.4 Radioactive Decay. We now give another example leading to a differential equation, which is the name for any equation involving derivatives, like equation (12) of the preceding section. Any radioactive material disintegrates by giving off radiation, and there remains a substance of lower atomic weight. If we make the reasonable assumption that the amount of radiation is proportional to the amount of radioactive material present at any time, it follows that the rate of decrease of the radioactive substance is proportional to the amount of radioactive substance remaining at any given time.

To translate this observation into mathematical symbols, let u denote the amount of radioactive substance present in a sample of material at any time t, so that u, being dependent on t, is a function of t. As time passes, u decreases, and since du/dt is the rate at which u changes, this derivative is negative. But the rate at which u changes is proportional to u, say $-ku$, where a minus sign is included since the rate of change is negative. Thus k is some positive constant of proportionality, and we have the differential equation

$$(15) \qquad \frac{du}{dt} = -ku \quad \text{or} \quad \frac{1}{u} \cdot \frac{du}{dt} = -k.$$

In the absence of a systematic treatment of differential equations, again as with equation (12) we find a solution by introducing a new variable. If we define $y = \log u$, then by Theorem 3 of § 7.3 we have

$$\frac{dy}{du} = \frac{1}{u}.$$

Now by Theorem 11 of § 4.5, with t in place of x, we see that

$$\frac{dy}{dt} = \frac{dy}{du} \cdot \frac{du}{dt} = \frac{1}{u} \cdot \frac{du}{dt}.$$

Combining this with (15) we obtain $dy/dt = -k$, and this is a differential equation whose solution is readily available, namely

$$y = -kt + c.$$

By including the constant c in this equation, we know that we have the most general representation of y as a function of t, by Theorem 7 of § 5.4. Now y is the same as $\log u$, so the solution of (15) is

$$(16) \qquad \log u = -kt + c.$$

This equation is equivalent to

$$(17) \qquad u = e^{-kt+c},$$

and this gives u as a function of t.

The constants c and k can be determined for any given sample of radioactive material by experimental data. For suppose we measure the amount of radioactive material at an initial time $t = 0$ and again at some later time t_1, finding that the amount is u_0 at time $t = 0$ and u_1 at $t = t_1$. Now if k and c are properly chosen, (16) gives the amount u of radioactive material present at time t for all values of t. At $t = 0$, equation (16) asserts that $\log u = c$. Since the amount u is u_0 at

$t = 0$ we have $\log u_0 = c$, which tells us the value of c. Similarly at $t = t_1$ we find from equation (16) that $\log u_1 = -kt_1 + c$. These results enable us to determine k as well as c, in the following way:

$$c = \log u_0, \quad \log u_1 = -kt_1 + c,$$
$$\log u_1 = -kt_1 + \log u_0,$$
$$k = \frac{\log u_0 - \log u_1}{t_1} = \frac{\log(u_0/u_1)}{t_1}.$$

Thus we have expressed c and k in terms of u_0, u_1, and t_1.

In numerical problems, it is not always necessary to evaluate k itself. For example, suppose we know that $u = 10$ when $t = 0$, and $u = 9$ when $t = 50$, and we want to find the value of u when $t = 150$. Then (17) gives

$$10 = e^c, \quad 9 = e^{c-50k}, \quad u = e^{c-150k}.$$

The first two equations imply that $e^{-50k} = \frac{9}{10}$ and so we get

$$u = e^c \cdot e^{-150k} = 10 \cdot \left(\frac{9}{10}\right)^3 = 7.29.$$

Problems

1. By substituting u_0 for u when $t = 0$ in (17), prove that (17) can be rewritten as $u = u_0 e^{-kt}$.

2. Verify that if equation (17) is differentiated, the result is (15).

3. A capsule contained 20 milligrams of a certain radioactive substance 60 years ago. Disintegration has reduced the amount to 19 milligrams today. How much will remain 240 years hence?

8.5 A Mixing Problem. To keep matters from getting too complicated, we shall examine a very specific mixing problem. Consider a tank containing 1200 gallons of brine, at a concentration of 1 pound of salt per gallon. Suppose that pure water is poured steadily into the tank at a rate of 20 gallons per minute; that the mixture is kept at a uniform concentration throughout the tank by vigorous stirring; and that the mixture flows steadily out of the tank also at a rate of 20 gallons per minute, so that the total volume under consideration is a constant 1200 gallons. The question is, what is the amount of salt in the tank at any time t? We may presume that t is measured in minutes, and that $t = 0$ at the time that the pure water started pouring into the tank.

Let there be x pounds of salt in the mixture in the tank at any time t, so that $x = 1200$ when $t = 0$. Then from time t to a later time $t + \Delta t$ the amount of salt in the tank decreases from x to $x + \Delta x$, where Δt is positive but Δx is negative. At time t the amount of salt per gallon of the mixture is $x/1200$, and at time $t + \Delta t$ the amount is $(x + \Delta x)/1200$. Over a time interval Δt, exactly $20(\Delta t)$ gallons of water enter the tank, and at the same time $20(\Delta t)$ gallons of the mixture leave the tank. This outflow of $20(\Delta t)$ gallons contains between

$$\frac{x}{1200} \cdot 20(\Delta t) \quad \text{and} \quad \frac{x + \Delta x}{1200} \cdot 20(\Delta t)$$

pounds of salt. The second of these is the smaller because Δx is negative. But the change in the amount of salt in the tank from time t to time $t + \Delta t$ is Δx; in other words the amount of salt leaving the tank in this time interval is $-\Delta x$ pounds. Hence we conclude that

$$\frac{x}{1200} \cdot 20(\Delta t) > -\Delta x > \frac{x + \Delta x}{1200} \cdot 20(\Delta t).$$

Dividing by Δt, we get

$$\frac{x}{60} > -\frac{\Delta x}{\Delta t} > \frac{x + \Delta x}{60}.$$

Taking limits as Δt and Δx tend to zero, we see that

$$\frac{x}{60} = -\frac{dx}{dt}, \quad \frac{dx}{dt} = -\frac{x}{60}, \quad \frac{1}{x} \cdot \frac{dx}{dt} = -\frac{1}{60}.$$

Notice that this amounts to the differential equation (15) of the preceding section, with x in place of u, and $\frac{1}{60}$ in place of k. Consequently we can go at once to the solution (17) of (15), which gives, when adapted to the present situation,

$$x = e^{c-t/60} = e^c \cdot e^{-t/60}.$$

Using the information that $x = 1200$ when $t = 0$, we see that $1200 = e^c$, and so the above equation becomes

$$x = 1200\,e^{-t/60}.$$

This equation represents the amount of salt x as a function of the time t, valid for $t \geq 0$.

Problems

The reader will find tables of natural logarithms and the exponential function of considerable use for the following problems.

1. With reference to the problem outlined above, how much salt remains in the tank after the pure water has been pouring in for 1 hour? for 2 hours?

2. At what time will the concentration of salt in the tank be $\frac{1}{2}$ pound per gallon? $\frac{1}{4}$ pound per gallon?

3. Draw a rough graph of the equation $x = 1200e^{-t/60}$ from, say, $t = 0$ to $t = 180$. Suggestion: The units of length on the axes should be carefully chosen; the t-axis should be horizontal, the x-axis vertical.

8.6 The Focusing Property of the Parabola. The parabola $y = x^2$ was used to illustrate some basic problems in calculus in earlier chapters. This particular equation can be regarded as a special case of $4py = x^2$, with $p = \frac{1}{4}$. If we choose another value for p, say $p = 1$, we get another parabola of a different size, $4y = x^2$. Thus the equation $4py = x^2$, or $y = x^2/(4p)$, is a general formula which includes all possible parabolas as p is given different positive values. The following analysis can be simplified if p is assigned the value 1 throughout; our reason for not taking $p = 1$ is that we want to establish the focusing property for all parabolas, not just for the parabola $4y = x^2$.

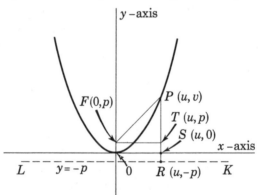

FIG. 8.2   Graph of $x^2 = 4py$.

In Figure 8.2 an arbitrary point P with coordinates (u, v) is selected on the parabola $x^2 = 4py$. The coordinates u and v are thus related by the equation $u^2 = 4pv$, and this relation will be used several times. The fixed point F with coordinates $(0, p)$ is called the *focus* of the parabola. The line LK is drawn parallel to the x-axis, at a distance p below. Hence the equation of the line LK is $y = -p$, since the y coordinate of every point on this line is $-p$. What we want to establish first is the following property of the parabola: that every point on the curve is equally distant from F and from the line LK. In Figure 8.2 a perpendicular PR is drawn from the point P to the line LK, intersecting the line LK at R. Thus the property to be proved can be written in the form of an equation, PF = PR.

The line LK, with equation $y = -p$, is called the *directrix* of the parabola. The property PF = PR states that every point P on the parabola is equally distant from a fixed point, the focus, and a fixed line, the directrix. Now whereas we prove this property PF = PR as a consequence of the equation $x^2 = 4py$ (or $u^2 = 4pv$), the parabola is often approached the other way around in books on geometry. That is to say, the parabola can be defined as the set of points (in a plane) equally distant from a fixed point and a fixed line (in the plane). Then the relation $x^2 = 4py$ can be proved as a property, provided the axes are located properly. The logic is correct no matter which is the definition and which the proved property. For our purposes it is most convenient to define the parabola in terms of its equation, and then derive the property PF = PR as a consequence.

Proof that PF = PR. Again with reference to Figure 8.2, let the line PR intersect the x-axis at the point S, whose coordinates are clearly $(u, 0)$. Finally, let a perpendicular FT be drawn from the focus F to the line PR; the coordinates of T are seen to be (u, p). We note the relations

$$PS = v, \quad TS = p, \quad PT = v-p, \quad PR = v+p, \quad FT = OS = u.$$

Using Pythagoras' theorem applied to the triangle PFT we get

$$PF^2 = PT^2 + FT^2 = (v-p)^2 + u^2 = v^2 - 2pv + p^2 + 4pv = (v+p)^2.$$

It follows that $PF^2 = PR^2$, and so $PF = PR = v+p$.

We now turn to a second geometric property of the parabola, namely that the tangent line to the parabola at the point P makes equal angles with PF and PQ, where PQ is the line through P parallel to the y-axis, as illustrated in Figure 8.3. Our plan is to prove this geometric result, and then interpret its meaning as "the focusing property of the parabola".

Let the tangent line to the parabola at the point P intersect the y-axis at B, so that as shown in Figure 8.3, APB is the tangent line. Then the geometric property under discussion is that $\angle FPB = \angle QPA$, and this we now prove. As a preliminary, we establish

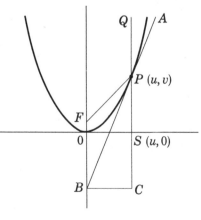

Fig. 8.3

that FP = FB. We differentiate the equation

$$y = \frac{1}{4p}x^2$$

to get

$$\frac{dy}{dx} = \frac{1}{4p}(2x) = \frac{x}{2p}.$$

Hence the slope of the line PB is $u/(2p)$, since u is the x coordinate of P. But the slope of PB is also PC/BC, and consequently

$$\frac{u}{2p} = \frac{PC}{BC} = \frac{PS+SC}{BC} = \frac{PS+OB}{OS} = \frac{v+OB}{u}.$$

Multiplying by u we get

$$\frac{u^2}{2p} = v+OB, \quad OB = \frac{u^2}{2p} - v = \frac{4pv}{2p} - v = 2v - v = v.$$

Hence the length of FB is expressible as

$$FB = FO + OB = p + v.$$

But FP = $p + v$ also, so FP = FB. Thus the triangle FPB is isosceles, and $\angle FPB = \angle FBP$. But $\angle FBP = \angle QPA$, and so $\angle FPB = \angle QPA$, which is what we wanted to prove.

Hence if we conceive of a ray of light emanating from F along the

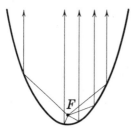

line FP, it will be reflected at P along the line PQ. Let a mirror be formed by revolving the parabola about the y-axis. Then the light rays emanating from F will be reflected by the mirror along paths parallel to the y-axis, as in Figure 8.4. A spotlight results from putting a light source at F.

Fig. 8.4

Or, if we think of the light moving in the other direction, the parabolic mirror will focus the light at the point F. Thus in a reflecting telescope the eye or the camera is located at point F.

Problems

1. Figure 8.2 has been drawn with the point P "above" the point T, i.e., with $v > p$. Prove that PF = PR in case $v < p$; also in case $v = p$. Draw diagrams in both cases.

2. What are the coordinates of the focus of the parabola $y = 2x^2$? of the parabola $6y = x^2$? of the parabola $6x = y^2$?

8.7 Newton's Method for Solving Equations. Consider the equation

(18) $$x^3 - 3x - 12 = 0.$$

This equation can be solved by exact methods, that is by methods yielding solutions in terms of radicals in the same sense that the formula

$$x = \frac{-b \pm \sqrt{b^2 - 4ac}}{2a}$$

is an exact solution of the equation $ax^2 + bx + c = 0$. If we are looking for a solution of (18) which is accurate only to a few decimal places, it is usually quicker to solve the problem by the use of an approximation method, such as the one we are about to describe, than to use the exact solution. Furthermore, while there is an exact solution of cubic equations like (18), and more generally there is a solution in terms of radicals for equations of degree 4 or less, it is known that it is impossible to solve the general equation of degree 5 or more by means of radicals. Hence to solve an equation such as $x^5 - 2x^4 + 2x^3 - 3x^2 + 1 = 0$, we would use an approximation method.

Returning to equation (18), let us denote $x^3 - 3x - 12$ by $f(x)$, and we can readily compute the following values:

$$f(-2) = -14, \quad f(-1) = -10, \quad f(0) = -12, \quad f(1) = -14,$$

$$f(2) = -10, \quad f(3) = 6.$$

The pair of functional values $f(2) = -10$ and $f(3) = 6$ suggests that as x varies continuously from $x = 2$ to $x = 3$, $f(x)$ varies continuously from -10 to 6, and so there is some intermediate value of x where $f(x) = 0$. This is so, and although it is perhaps intuitively obvious, it is not easy to give a rigorous mathematical proof. We give no proof here, but simply take it as axiomatic that if a continuous function $f(x)$ has functional values $f(a)$ and $f(b)$ with opposite signs, then there is at least one value of x between a and b for which $f(x) = 0$. Thus equation (18) has a root between $x = 2$ and $x = 3$, and we can take either of these as a first approximation to the root. The approximation $x = 3$ is preferable, because 6 is closer to 0 than -10 is.

In general, suppose we have a first approximation $x = a$ to a root of an equation $f(x) = 0$. The idea is that we will use a tangent line to the curve $y = f(x)$ at the point where $x = a$, as illustrated in Figure 8.5, to get a better approximation to the root. In Figure 8.5, P is the point where the graph of $y = f(x)$ crosses the x-axis, so the x coordinate of the unknown point P is the root of $f(x) = 0$ that we are trying to approximate. Beginning with the approximation $x = a$, we draw a tangent line to the curve at the point A with coordinates $(a, f(a))$. This is the line AB, and the point B on the x-axis has an x coordinate which is in general a better approximation than $x = a$. Repeating the process, we use a tangent line at C to get to the point D, whose x coordinate gives a still better approximation.

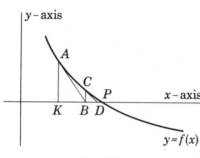

Fig. 8.5

This geometrical process leads to a simple formula by the following analysis. The slope of the line AB equals the value of the derivative $f'(x)$ at $x = a$, namely $f'(a)$. But if we use $(b, 0)$ as the coordinates of B, the slope of the line AB is also seen to be, from equation (1) of § 1.1,

$$\frac{0 - f(a)}{b - a}, \quad \text{and so} \quad \frac{0 - f(a)}{b - a} = f'(a).$$

Using simple algebra, we get

$$-f(a) = (b - a)f'(a), \quad b - a = -\frac{f(a)}{f'(a)},$$

$$(19) \qquad\qquad b = a - \frac{f(a)}{f'(a)},$$

Thus from a first approximation $x = a$ we get a second approximation $x = b$ as in (19), and this in turn gives a third approximation $x = c$, where

$$c = b - \frac{f(b)}{f'(b)}, \quad \text{etc.}$$

Returning to equation (18) as an application of the use of (19), we have

$$f(x) = x^3 - 3x - 12, \quad f'(x) = 3x^2 - 3, \quad a = 3,$$

$$f(a) = 6, \quad f'(a) = 24, \quad b = a - \frac{f(a)}{f'(a)} = 3 - \frac{6}{24} = \frac{11}{4}.$$

Turning to decimals at the next stage, we get

$$c = b - \frac{f(b)}{f'(b)} = 2.75 - \frac{.55}{19.7} \cong 2.72,$$

to two decimal places.

Had we started with the approximation $a = 2$, we would have obtained

$$f(2) = -10, \quad f'(2) = 9, \quad b = a - \frac{f(a)}{f'(a)} = 2 - \frac{-10}{9} \cong 3.1.$$

We appear to be losing ground, but 3.1 is actually a better approximation than 2 is. A repetition of the process would lead from 3.1 back toward the root.

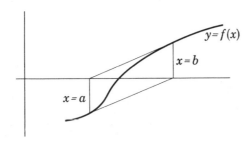

FIG. 8.6

The use of (19) will not always give a succession of values $a, b, c, \ldots$ which converge to the actual root. For example, in Figure 8.6 there is an example of a function such that the approximation a leads to b, but iteration of the process leads back to a again. The mathematical theory giving conditions under which success of the procedure is assured is beyond the scope of this book. We shall confine our attention to cases where the successive approximations *do* lead to the root with increasing accuracy. To minimize the amount of calculation required, we shall require accuracy to two decimal places only. When two successive approximations are identical to two decimal places, we shall regard this as assurance of accuracy. For example, in the case of the equation (18), we obtain 2.72 as an approximation to the root after two applications of (19). Another iteration of the process leads from 2.72 to the same number, 2.72, to two decimal places of accuracy. Hence we conclude that 2.72 is a root of $x^3 - 3x - 12 = 0$, accurate to two decimal places.

Newton's method is not restricted to the solution of polynomial equations, but can also be applied to such equations as $\sin x = x/2$

and $e^x = x + 7$. No new idea is involved in such applications, so we shall confine attention to polynomials, for ease of computation.

Problems

1. By drawing a rough sketch of the graph of $y = x^3 - 3x - 12$, establish that equation (18) has only one real root. Suggestion: The derivative of $f(x) = x^3 - 3x - 12$ is $f'(x) = 3x^2 - 3$, and so by the theory of § 4.7 the curve has a local maximum point at $(-1, -10)$ and a local minimum point at $(1, -14)$. Furthermore, as x increases, $f(x)$ is increasing for $x < -1$ and $x > 1$, but $f(x)$ is decreasing for $-1 < x < 1$.

2. Establish that $x^3 + x - 5 = 0$ has only one real root, and that this root lies between $x = 1$ and $x = 2$. Find the root to two decimal places of accuracy.

3. Find all real roots of $x^3 + x^2 - 7 = 0$.

4. Establish that the equation $x^3 + 12x^2 + 36x - 4 = 0$ has only one real root, and that this root lies between $x = 0$ and $x = 1$. Find this root to two decimal places of accuracy.

5. Find all real roots of $x^3 + 3x^2 + x - 6 = 0$ to two decimal places of accuracy.

6. Find all real roots of $x^3 - 3x^2 - x + 4 = 0$ to two decimal places.

7. Find the value of $\sqrt{3}$ to two decimal places by solving the equation $x^2 - 3 = 0$ by Newton's method.

8. Evaluate $\sqrt[3]{30}$ to two decimal places.

*9. (a) Let k and a be positive numbers such that a is an approximation to $\sqrt{k}$. Prove that Newton's method applied to the equation $x^2 - k = 0$ gives $\frac{1}{2}(a + k/a)$ as the next approximation.

(b) Prove that the approximation $\frac{1}{2}(a + k/a)$ is larger than $\sqrt{k}$, whether or not a is larger than $\sqrt{k}$. Suggestion: The inequality $\frac{1}{2}(a + k/a) > \sqrt{k}$ is equivalent to $a + k/a > 2\sqrt{k}$, $a - 2\sqrt{k} + k/a > 0$, $(\sqrt{a} - \sqrt{k/a})^2 > 0$.

(c) Suppose that the approximation a is too large, i.e., $a > \sqrt{k}$. Prove that $\frac{1}{2}(a + k/a)$ is a better approximation in the sense that it is closer to $\sqrt{k}$; that is, prove that

$$\tfrac{1}{2}(a + k/a) - \sqrt{k} < a - \sqrt{k}.$$

(d) Suppose that the approximation a is too small, i.e., $a < \sqrt{k}$, but large enough so that $3a > \sqrt{k}$. Prove that $\frac{1}{2}(a + k/a)$ is a better approximation; that is, prove that

$$\tfrac{1}{2}(a + k/a) - \sqrt{k} < \sqrt{k} - a.$$

Suggestion: This inequality is equivalent to $a + k/a - 2\sqrt{k} < 2\sqrt{k} - 2a$, $3a - 4\sqrt{k} + k/a < 0$, and

$$\frac{(3a - \sqrt{k})(a - \sqrt{k})}{a} < 0.$$

*10. Let a be an approximation to $\sqrt[3]{k}$. Prove that Newton's method applied to $x^3 - k = 0$ gives $\frac{1}{3}(2a + k/a^2)$ as the next approximation.

APPENDIX A

ON THE EXISTENCE OF THE DEFINITE INTEGRAL

In § 5.3 we established the existence of the definite integral

(1) $$\int_a^b f(x)\, dx,$$

but only in the presence of a function $F(x)$ whose derivative $F'(x)$ is equal to $f(x)$. In the case of such an integral as

$$\int_1^2 \sqrt{x^3 + 1}\, dx$$

we know of no function $F(x)$ whose derivative is $\sqrt{x^3 + 1}$. Nevertheless this integral exists, as we shall now show. The general result that we establish is this: *the integral* (1), *as defined in equation* (2) *of* § 5.2, *or equation* (4) *of* § 3.2, *exists for any monotonic function* $f(x)$.

The existence proof that we are about to give is necessary in order to complete the argument of Chapter 7, where we defined the function $L(x)$ by the integral

$$L(x) = \int_1^x \frac{dv}{v}.$$

We now establish that $L(x)$ really exists, and so we will have a proper foundation for the logarithmic and exponential functions.

The proof is given for a monotonic increasing function $f(x)$. For a monotonic decreasing function the proof is analogous with all inequalities reversed.

In the course of the proof we shall use a fundamental proposition about real numbers, which we now explain. It will be labeled an "axiom", although in any thorough study of the real number system it can be given as a theorem, i.e., it can be proved. We say that a sequence $a_1, a_2, a_3, a_4, \ldots$ is non-decreasing in case $a_1 \leqq a_2$, $a_2 \leqq a_3$, $a_3 \leqq a_4$, etc. The sequence is non-increasing in case all the reverse inequalities hold. A sequence is bounded above if there is a constant c such that $a_1 < c$, $a_2 < c$, $a_3 < c$, etc. Similarly a sequence is bounded below if there is a constant k such that $k < a_1$, $k < a_2$, $k < a_3$, etc.

For example consider the sequences

(2) $$1, 2, 3, 4, 5, 6, 7, 8, \ldots,$$

(3) $$\frac{1}{2}, \frac{2}{3}, \frac{3}{4}, \frac{4}{5}, \frac{5}{6}, \frac{6}{7}, \frac{7}{8}, \ldots,$$

(4) $$\frac{1}{2}, \frac{2}{2^2}, \frac{3}{2^3}, \frac{4}{2^4}, \frac{5}{2^5}, \frac{6}{2^6}, \frac{7}{2^7}, \ldots.$$

The sequence (2) is non-decreasing, but is not bounded above, although it is bounded below. (The sequence (2) is actually increasing, but "non-decreasing" is a more useful concept in this Appendix.) The sequence (3) is non-decreasing and is bounded above and below. The sequence (4) is non-increasing and is bounded above and below.

AXIOM ON BOUNDED SEQUENCES. *A non-decreasing sequence that is bounded above has a limit. A non-increasing sequence that is bounded below has a limit.*

This axiom has nothing to say about the sequence (2) above, but it applies to the sequences (3) and (4) and assures us that these sequences have limits. The limits are 1 and 0 respectively, but the axiom only assures us of the existence of a limit, not that we can find the actual limit in all cases.

We shall use this axiom later in the proof, but first we prove a result about limits.

THEOREM 1. *If the terms of the sequences $\{a_n\}$, $\{b_n\}$ and $\{c_n\}$ satisfy the inequalities $b_n \leqq a_n \leqq c_n$ for all positive integers n, and if $a_n \to k$ and $c_n - b_n \to 0$ as $n \to \infty$, then $b_n \to k$ and $c_n \to k$.*

PROOF. Noting that

$$0 \leqq a_n - b_n \leqq c_n - b_n$$

we see that $a_n - b_n \to 0$ by Theorem 9 of § 2.3. Then by Corollary 13 of § 2.4 we conclude that $b_n \to k$. Also $c_n - b_n \to 0$ implies that $b_n - c_n \to 0$, and so the same Corollary 13 implies that $c_n \to k$.

It will be convenient to use some simple notation from the theory of sets. By a set C we mean a collection of elements; all the sets we use will have real numbers for elements. If C and C' are two sets we will write $C \subset C'$ in case every element of C is also an element of C'. For example if C comprises the elements 1, 3, 5, 7 and C' comprises 1, 3, 5, 7, 9, 11, then we can write $C \subset C'$.

The notation $C \cup C'$ will denote the union of the sets C and C', that is, the set of all elements which are in C or in C'. For example if C comprises the elements 1, 3, 7 and C' comprises 3, 5, 9, 13, then the set $C \cup C'$ comprises the elements 1, 3, 5, 7, 9, 13. In this example it is not true that $C \subset C'$.

Now the sets that we discuss come from the definition of an integral in § 5.2, namely

$$(5) \qquad \int_a^b f(x)\,dx = \lim_{n \to \infty} \sum_{j=1}^{n} (x_j - x_{j-1}) f(\xi_j),$$

where $a = x_0 \leq x_1 \leq x_2 \leq \ldots \leq x_{n-1} \leq x_n = b$, and $x_{j-1} \leq \xi_j \leq x_j$. We write C_n for the set of real numbers $a, x_1, x_2, \ldots, x_{n-1}, b$. Every set that we discuss will contain the numbers a and b. Furthermore, every set will contain only a finite number of elements, and no set will contain any number less than a or any number greater than b.

The upper and lower sums, S_n and s_n, of equations (3) and (4) of § 5.2, are now assigned new notation:

$$S(C_n) = (x_1 - x_0) f(x_1) + (x_2 - x_1) f(x_2) + \ldots + (x_n - x_{n-1}) f(x_n),$$
$$s(C_n) = (x_1 - x_0) f(x_0) + (x_2 - x_1) f(x_1) + \ldots + (x_n - x_{n-1}) f(x_{n-1}).$$

Hence Theorem 2 of § 5.2 can be reformulated thus: If $f(x)$ is a monotonic function, then

$$(6) \qquad \lim_{n \to \infty} \{S(C_n) - s(C_n)\} = 0.$$

In general if C is any set of numbers including a and b say

$$(7) \qquad C : a, z_1, z_2, z_3, \ldots, z_{r-1}, b,$$

where

$$a = z_0 \leq z_1 \leq z_2 \leq z_3 \leq \ldots \leq z_{r-1} \leq z_r = b,$$

then we define $s(C)$ and $S(C)$ by the equations

$$(8) \qquad s(C) = (z_1 - z_0) f(z_0) + (z_2 - z_1) f(z_1) + \ldots + (z_r - z_{r-1}) f(z_{r-1}),$$
$$(9) \qquad S(C) = (z_1 - z_0) f(z_1) + (z_2 - z_1) f(z_2) + \ldots + (z_r - z_{r-1}) f(z_r).$$

THEOREM 2. *If $f(x)$ is monotonic increasing over $a \leq x \leq b$, and if $C \subset C'$, then*

$$s(C) \leq s(C') \quad and \quad S(C) \geq S(C').$$

PROOF. It suffices to establish these results in case the set C' contains exactly one more real number than does C. For then we can work from C to C' in general by bringing in one new element at a time, step by step from C to C'.

So let us suppose that C is as given in (7), and let us write C' as the same set with the addition of one new element u,

$$C' : a, z_1, z_2, z_3, \dots, z_j, u, z_{j+1}, \dots z_{r-1}, b,$$

with $z_j \leq u \leq z_{j+1}$. Then $s(C')$ is the same as $s(C)$ except that the term $(z_{j+1}-z_j)f(z_j)$ is replaced by

$$(u - z_j)f(z_j) + (z_{j+1} - u)f(u).$$

Thus to prove that $s(C) \leq s(C')$ we must establish that

(10) $(z_{j+1} - z_j)f(z_j) \leq (u - z_j)f(z_j) + (z_{j+1} - u)f(u).$

Bringing the terms involving $f(z_j)$ together on the left, we see that (10) amounts to

(11) $(z_{j+1} - u)f(z_j) \leq (z_{j+1} - u)f(u).$

Now $z_{j+1} - u$ is non-negative, and $f(z_j) \leq f(u)$ since f is a monotonic increasing function, and so (11) and (10) are established.

As to $S(C) \geq S(C')$, the proof is much the same. In place of (10) we want to prove

$$(z_{j+1} - z_j)f(z_{j+1}) \geq (u - z_j)f(u) + (z_{j+1} - u)f(z_{j+1}),$$

which reduces to

$$(u - z_j)f(z_{j+1}) \geq (u - z_j)f(u).$$

This can be established in the same way as was (11).

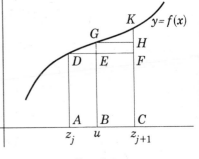

There is a simple geometric interpretation of (10), shown in Figure A.1. The functional values $f(z_j), f(u),$ and $f(z_{j+1})$ are represented by the lengths AD, BG, and CK. Inequality (10) simply asserts that the area of the rectangle ACFD is not more than the sum of the areas of the rectangles ABED and BCHG.

FIG. A.1

Next consider once again the definition (5) of the integral. For each positive integer n, the set C_n consists of $n+1$ points a, x_1, x_2, ..., x_{n-1}, b. Define $C_n{}^*$ as the union of all sets C_1, C_2, ..., C_n, thus

(12) $$C_n{}^* = C_1 \cup C_2 \cup C_3 \cup ... \cup C_n.$$

In other words, $C_n{}^*$ consists of all numbers in all the sets C_1, C_2, ..., C_n. It follows at once that

$$C_1{}^* \subset C_2{}^* \subset C_3{}^* \subset C_4{}^* \subset ... \subset C_n{}^* \subset ...,$$

and so from Theorem 2

(13) $$s(C_1{}^*) \leqq s(C_2{}^*) \leqq s(C_3{}^*) \leqq s(C_4{}^*) \leqq ....$$

In order to apply the Axiom on Bounded Sequences, we want to show that the sequence (13) is bounded. Every term in (13) is of the form (8), and since $f(x) \leqq f(b)$ for all x satisfying $a \leqq x \leqq b$, we see that

$$(z_1 - z_0)f(z_0) + (z_2 - z_1)f(z_1) + ... + (z_r - z_{r-1})f(z_{r-1})$$
$$\leqq (z_1 - z_0)f(b) + (z_2 - z_1)f(b) + ... + (z_r - z_{r-1})f(b)$$
$$= f(b)[(z_1 - z_0) + (z_2 - z_1) + ... + (z_r - z_{r-1})]$$
$$= f(b)[z_n - z_0] = f(b)[b - a].$$

Now $f(b)$ and $b - a$ are fixed, and so the terms of (13) are bounded above. Hence $s(C_n{}^*)$ tends to a limit, say k, as n tends to infinity.

Next we observe that

$$s(C_n) \leqq s(C_n{}^*) \leqq S(C_n{}^*) \leqq S(C_n).$$

The first and last of these follow from (12) and Theorem 2. The middle inequality can be seen at once from (8) and (9), since $f(x)$ is monotonic increasing. Applying equation (6) and Theorem 1 with b_n, a_n, and c_n replaced by $s(C_n)$, $s(C_n{}^*)$ and $S(C_n)$, we conclude that as $n \to \infty$,

$$s(C_n) \to k, \quad S(C_n) \to k.$$

Reverting to our earlier notation, we can rewrite these in the forms $s_n \to k$, $S_n \to k$. Then by Theorem 1 of § 5.2 we have $s_n \leqq \sigma_n \leqq S_n$, where σ_n is defined by

$$\sigma_n = \sum_{j=1}^{n} (x_j - x_{j-1})f(\xi_j).$$

Applying Theorem 17 of § 2.4 we conclude that $\sigma_n \to k$. Thus we have established the existence of the integral because it is, by equation (5), the limit of σ_n.

ANSWERS TO ODD-NUMBERED PROBLEMS

Section 1.1, page 3
3. $7/2$
11. $(-4, -11)$
15. d/c

Section 1.2, page 6
1. $S = 36\pi/h + 6\pi\sqrt{2h}$
5. 30, 72, 2, 20
7. $5, -11, -3, -30, -23/8$

Section 1.3, page 8
1. 12
3. 2
7. 12
9. 3

Section 1.4, page 10
Among the odd-numbered problems, these are incorrect: 11, 13

Section 1.5, page 13
1. 500500
3. 297925
7. (a) $\frac{1}{3}n^3 - \frac{1}{2}n^2 + \frac{1}{6}n$
  (b) $\frac{1}{3}n^3 - \frac{3}{2}n^2 + \frac{13}{6}n - 1$

Section 1.6, page 16
1. $\frac{2}{3}$
3. $\frac{1}{6}$
5. $\frac{8}{3}$
7. 8

Section 1.8, page 19
1. (a) 1 (b) $-\frac{2}{3}$ (c) 0
7. $(1, 4)$ and $(-\frac{3}{4}, \frac{9}{4})$
9. $(4, -3), (1, 7)$, and $(-2, 17)$
11. $y = x - 3$
13. $x^2 + y^2 = 25$; yes
15. $y = 6x - 9$

Section 2.1, page 24
1. $a = 5, b = 2, c = -4$
  will do
3. $a = 5, b = -5$, will do
11. (i), (iv) and (v) are false

Section 2.2, page 28
3. These will do:
  $100 < x < 200$;
  $200 > x > 100$;
  $|x - 150| < 50$;
  $50 > |x - 150|$
5. These will do:
  $70 \leq T \leq 74$;
  $74 \geq T \geq 70$;
  $|T - 72| \leq 2$;
  $|72 - T| \leq 2$
7. These will do:
  $|x - y| \leq \epsilon$;
  $|y - x| \leq \epsilon$;
  $\epsilon \geq |x - y|$;
  $\epsilon \geq |y - x|$;
  $-\epsilon \leq x - y \leq \epsilon$;
  $-\epsilon \leq y - x \leq \epsilon$;
  $\epsilon \geq x - y \geq -\epsilon$;
  $\epsilon \geq y - x \geq -\epsilon$

9. (a) $|x| < 9$
   (b) $|x| \leqq 9$
   (c) $|x-22| < 8$
   (d) $|x-16| < 4$
   (e) $|x-3| < 4$
   (f) $|x-1| < 2$
11. $-2 < x < 7$
13. $x > 6$ or $x < 1$
15. $-6 < x < 7$
17. $x > 5$ or $x < 1$

Section 2.3, page 33

1. (a) 0   (d) none
   (b) 0   (e) 1
   (c) 1   (f) 0
3. (i) $-a$ (iii) $\frac{1}{2}a$
   (ii) $1+a$ (iv) 0
5. (1) a (2) a
9. This will do:
   $4+\frac{1}{2}, 4+\frac{1}{3}, 4+\frac{1}{4}, 4+\frac{1}{5}, \ldots$

Section 2.4, page 37

1. (a) 2   (e) 4
   (b) 4   (f) $\frac{1}{3}$
   (c) 0   (g) $\frac{1}{3}$
   (d) 1
3. (i) $3a$ (iii) 0
   (ii) $b-2a$ (iv) $a+b$
9. $(a+b)/2$

Section 2.5, page 41

1. (a) $0 < x < \infty$
   (b) $0 \leqq x < \infty$
   (c) $-\infty < x < 0$
3. $f(1) = 3, f(2) = 6, f(3) = 13,$
   $f(4) = 24, f(0) = 4,$
   $f(-1) = 9$

5. $f(2) = 13, f(5) = 22,$
   $f(c) = 3c+7, f(2c) = 6c+7,$
   $f(2x) = 6x+7,$
   $f(2x+6) = 6x+25,$
   $f(g(x)) = 6x+25,$
   $g(f(x)) = 6x+20$
7. $g(x) = 2x-9$
9. Range: $-\infty < f(x) < \infty$
11. Range: $-7 \leqq f(x) < \infty$

Section 2.6, page 44

7. $\dfrac{180}{\pi}, \dfrac{900}{\pi}, \dfrac{180x}{\pi}$

13. $1 + \cot^2 x = \operatorname{cosec}^2 x,$
    $1 + \tan^2 x = \sec^2 x$

Section 2.8, page 53

1. 1
3. 1 and 3
5. 0
9. (a) 5   (b) 1   (c) 1   (d) 3

Section 2.9, page 57

3. $f(0) \neq 0$
5. $\delta = .08$ will do

Section 3.1, page 62

1. $\frac{1}{2}$
3. 2
5. 1
7. 1

Section 3.2, page 67

3. $\displaystyle\int_2^8 f(x)\, dx$

5. $\frac{1}{2}$

Section 3.3, page 71

1. $\frac{7}{3}$, $\frac{124}{3}$, 42
3. $\frac{1}{4}$
5. $a^5/5$
7. $(b^3 - a^3)/3$, $(c^3 - a^3)/3$, $(b^3 - c^3)/3$

Section 3.4, page 74

1. (a) $\frac{1}{5}$ (e) $-21/2$
   (b) $\frac{2}{5}$ (f) $64/5$
   (c) $32/5$ (g) 0
   (d) $-31/5$ (h) 0
5. $\frac{2}{3}b^{3/2}$, $(2b^{3/2} - 2a^{3/2})/3$
7. $32/3$

Section 3.5, page 76

1. (a) $20/3$ (c) $14/3$
   (b) $4/3$ (d) 12
3. $b = 6$ and $b = -8$

Section 3.6, page 79

1. (a) $\dfrac{2 - \sqrt{3}}{2}$ (c) 2
   (b) 1 (d) $2(\sqrt{3} - 1)$
3. (a) 2 (c) $\dfrac{2 - \sqrt{2}}{2}$
   (b) $\dfrac{2 - \sqrt{2}}{2}$ (d) $2 + \dfrac{\pi^2}{2}$
5. $x = \pi/3$

Section 3.7, page 82

3. 24π
5. $\pi r^2 h$
7. $8\pi/3$

Section 4.1, page 87

1. (a) $dy/dx = 2x + 1$
   (b) $dy/dx = 4x$

(c) $dy/dx = 6x^2$
(d) $dy/dx = 3x^2 - 1$
3. $dy/dx = 4x^3$
5. $27x - y + 54 = 0$
7. (a) $(0, 0)$
   (b) $(0, 0)$ and $(2, 4)$
11. The x-coordinates of A and B must be the negatives of each other

Section 4.2, page 91

3. $\dfrac{dy}{dx} = \lim\limits_{\Delta x \to 0} \dfrac{\sin(x + \Delta x) - \sin x}{\Delta x}$
5. $2z$

Section 4.3, page 96

1. (a) $y' = 14x$
   (b) $y' = 14x$
   (c) $y' = 14x - 4$
   (d) $y' = 30x^5 - 4x^3$
   (e) $y' = -3x^{-4}$
   (f) $y' = -4x^{-5}$
   (g) $y' = 4$
   (h) $y' = 0$
5. (a) $y' = \dfrac{3}{(3 + x)^2}$
   (b) $y' = \dfrac{-x - 4}{x^3}$
   (c) $y' = \dfrac{6x - x^4}{(x^3 + 3)^2}$
   (d) $y' = \dfrac{x^2 - 7}{x^2}$
   (e) $y' = \dfrac{3 - x}{2\sqrt{x}(x + 3)^2}$
   (f) $y' = (6x + 14)/\sqrt{x}$
9. $y = cx^2$

Section 4.4, page 99

1. (a) $y' = -\csc x \cot x$
   (b) $y' = \sec x \tan x$
   (c) $y' = -\csc^2 x$
   (d) $y' = -5 \cos x$
   (e) $y' = (x \cos x - \sin x)/x^2$
   (f) $y' = \cos^2 x - \sin^2 x$
   (g) $y' = 2 \sin x \cos x$
   (h) $y' = 3 \sin^2 x \cos x$
   (i) $y' = -2 \sin x \cos x$
   (j) $y' = 0$
3. (a) $y' = \sin x + x \cos x$
   (b) $y' = 2x + \sin x$
   (c) $y' = (x \cos x - \sin x)/x^2$
   (d) $y' = \dfrac{(1+x)\sec^2 x - 2\tan x}{(1+x)^3}$
5. $x + 2y - \sqrt{3} - \pi/6 = 0$

Section 4.5, page 102

1. (a) $y' = -7 \sin 7x$
   (b) $y' = 3 \sec^2 3x$
   (c) $y' = \dfrac{1}{2\sqrt{x+1}}$
   (d) $y' = \dfrac{x}{\sqrt{x^2+1}}$
   (e) $y' = 18x^2(2+x^3)^5$
   (f) $y' = -2 \sin 2x$
   (g) $y' = -2 \cos x \sin x$
   (h) $y' = 7 \sin^6 x \cos x$
   (i) $y' = \dfrac{x}{(a^2+x^2)^{1/2}}$
   (j) $y' = \dfrac{x-c}{\{b^2+(c-x)^2\}^{1/2}}$
3. 20
5. $y' = -x/(25-x^2)^{1/2}$, $-\dfrac{3}{4}$
9. $\dfrac{1}{2\sqrt{x+3}}$

Section 4.6, page 108

3. None
5. (a) $y' = \frac{3}{4}x^{-1/4}$
   (b) $y' = -\frac{4}{5}x^{-9/5}$
   (c) $y' = \frac{2}{3}x^{-1/3}$
7. $y' = 1/\sqrt{1-x^2}$

Section 4.7, page 110

1. (i) $c = 1$ (iv) $c = \pi/2$
   (ii) $c = 1/2$ (v) $c = 2/3$
   (iii) $c = 3/2$

Section 4.8, page 114

1. y is a minimum if $x = 2$
   (b) y is a maximum if
   $x = 7/2$
   (c) y is a maximum if
   $x = -3$, a minimum if
   $x = 2$
   (d) y is a maximum if
   $x = -3$, a minimum if
   $x = 2$
   (e) None
   (f) None
   (g) y is a maximum if
   $x = -2$, a minimum if
   $x = 0$
   (h) y is a minimum if
   $x = \sqrt[3]{9/2}$
   (i) y is a minimum if
   $x = \sqrt[3]{9/2}$
3. 6 and 6
5. $p/4$ by $p/4$
7. $\sqrt{3}/3$
9. 19/2 and 1/2
11. $x = 15$, $y = 10$
13. (1, 1)
15. Height 3 inches, base
    12 inches by 12 inches.

Section 4.9, page 116

1. $r = 5/\sqrt[3]{\pi}, h = 10/\sqrt[3]{\pi}$
5. 6 inches by 8 inches
7. 4 units by 3 units
9. 12 units
11. Radius of base $10/\sqrt[3]{3\pi}$ feet, height $10\sqrt[3]{9/\pi}$ feet

Section 4.10, page 119

1. At a point $\sqrt{3}/6$ miles from Q

Section 5.2, page 124

1. $s_n = .8, \quad S_n = 1.2,$
$F(b) - F(a) = 1$
3. $s_n = .95, \quad S_n = 1.05,$
$F(b) - F(a) = 1$
5. $s_n = .855, \quad S_n = 1.155,$
$F(b) - F(a) = 1$

Section 5.3, page 128

5. (a) 2/3   (b) 2
7. (a) 43/15   (c) 1/12
    (b) $\sqrt{2}/2$ (d) 1

Section 5.4, page 131

1. $\frac{1}{2}x^2 + c$
3. $2x^2 - 2x^3 + c$
5. $\dfrac{-1}{2x^2} + c$
7. arc tan $x + c$.
9. $-\cos x + c$
11. $-\frac{1}{2}\cos 2x + c$
13. (a) $\frac{2}{3}x^{3/2} + c$
    (b) $\frac{3}{5}x^{5/3} + c$
    (c) $-\frac{1}{2}x^{-2} + c$
    (d) $\frac{1}{7}x^7 + \frac{2}{5}x^5 + \frac{1}{3}x^3 + c$

15. (a) $y = \frac{1}{4}x^4 + c$
     (b) $y = 2\sin x + c$

Section 6.2, page 142

1. .19867
3. .99863

9. $\cos^2 x = 1 - x^2 + \dfrac{x^4}{3}$
$\qquad - \dfrac{2x^6}{45} + \dfrac{x^8}{315} - \cdots$

Section 7.1, page 149

1. $L(5) - L(2),$ or $L(5/2)$
9. $\int_1^9 (dx/x)$

Section 7.3, page 157

1. e, e^2, e^3
3. (a) $y' = 1/x$
    (b) $y' = 1/x$
    (c) $y' = 1/(x+1)$
    (d) $y' = 2/(2x+1)$
5. $y' = 3/x$
7. (a) $e - 1$ (b) log 3
    (c) -1 (d) $1 + \log 2$
9. y is a minimum if $x = 1$
15. $1/(x+c);$
$\log(b+c) - \log(a+c)$
17. $xe^x; \quad 1$

Section 7.4, page 162

3. 1.10517
9. $f(x) = 4e^x$

Section 7.5, page 164

1. 2.25, 2.37, 2.44
3. (a) e (b) e^2
    (c) $\sqrt{e}$ (d) e^3
    (e) $\sqrt[3]{e}$ (f) e

Section 7.6, page 167

1. $-.1054$
3. $\log 1 = 0$

Section 7.7, page 169

1. (a) .4771   (b) .6990
   (c) .7782   (d) .2041
7. .631

Section 8.2, page 173

1. 3.1416
3. .0997
5. 1.1071

Section 8.4, page 180

3. 15.5 milligrams

Section 8.5, page 181

1. 441.5 lb., 162.4 lb.

Section 8.7, page 188

3. 1.63
5. 1.09
7. 1.73

INDEX